Holt McDougal Mathematics

Grade 8
Ready to Go On?
Intervention and Enrichment

HOLT McDOUGAL

HOUGHTON MIFFLIN HARCOURT

COMMON CORE
EDITION

Contents

Holt McDougal Mathematics

Contents

© Houghton Mifflin Harcourt Publishing Company

Holt McDougal Mathematics

Introduction

Using the Ready to Go On? Intervention and Enrichment

The *Ready to Go On? Intervention and Enrichment* helps students to perform successfully by providing opportunities for you to address students' weaknesses before the students are given summative assessments. The *Ready to Go On? Intervention* provides skills and problem-solving intervention for students having difficulty mastering concepts taught in the lessons.

Intervention

After teaching each section of lessons, have students complete the *Ready to Go On?* page in the student book. This page targets the lesson skills necessary for success in the chapter. For students requiring help, use the appropriate *Skills Intervention* or *Problem Solving Intervention* worksheets. Each worksheet provides step-by-step scaffolding prompts to help students understand the lesson concepts and skills.

A chart at the end of each section correlates the lessons with the appropriate intervention and enrichment materials. The chart appears in the Teacher Edition. A sample is shown below.

READY TO GO ON?
Diagnose and Prescribe

NO INTERVENE				YES ENRICH

Ready to Go On? Intervention	Ready to Go On? Intervention			Ready to Go On? Enrichment
	Worksheets	Online		Worksheets / Online
Lesson 1	1 Intervention	Activity 1		
Lesson 2	2 Intervention	Activity 2		
Lesson 3	3 Intervention	Activity 3	Diagnose and Prescribe Online	
Lesson 4	4 Intervention	Activity 4		
Lesson 5	5 Intervention	Activity 5		

Assessment

Use the *Section Quizzes* to assess the student's proficiency after you have provided Intervention, or use the *Section Quizzes* to assess the student's retention on the new concepts taught in the lessons.

Enrichment

For those students who show proficiency on the *Ready to Go On? Section Quizzes,* provide them with the appropriate *Section Enrichment* worksheets. The worksheets extend the concepts taught in the lessons.

Holt McDougal Mathematics

Individual Lesson Skills Checklist

Chapter	Lesson	Prescription	Skill Mastered

© Houghton Mifflin Harcourt Publishing Company

Holt McDougal Mathematics

Ready to Go On?

LESSON	# Rational Numbers

1 **Skills Intervention: Rational Numbers**

A **rational number** is any number that can be written as a fraction $\frac{n}{d}$, where n and d are integers and $d \neq 0$. Repeating and terminating decimals are rational numbers. When a fraction is in simplest form, the numerator and denominator are **relatively prime.** Relatively prime numbers have no common factors other than 1.

Vocabulary
rational number
relatively prime

$$\frac{6}{24} = \frac{1}{4} \qquad -0.\overline{5} = -\frac{5}{9} \qquad 0.2 = \frac{2}{10}$$

Simplifying Fractions

Write $\frac{8}{12}$ in simplest form.

$\frac{8}{12}$ What factor is common to 8 and 12? _____

$\dfrac{8 \underline{\quad}}{12 \underline{\quad}}$ How do you simplify the fraction? _____

_____

$\frac{2}{3}$ How do you know your answer is in simplest form?

_____

Writing Decimals as Fractions

Write each decimal as a fraction in simplest form.

A. -0.125

$-0.12\underline{}$ Which digit is farthest to the right? _____

What place value is the 5 in? _____

$-0.125 = \dfrac{\overline{}}{\underline{}}$ Write the decimal as a fraction.

$= \dfrac{-1}{8}$ _____ is the greatest common factor of 125 and 1000.

B. $\frac{8}{3}$

Use long division to write $\frac{8}{3}$ as a decimal.

Which number is the dividend? _____

How many times does 3 go into 8? _____

How many times does 3 go into 20? _____

$\dfrac{8}{3} = \underline{}.\overline{6}$

$$
\begin{array}{r}
\overset{.}{}\overline{} \\
3)\overline{.00} \\
\underline{-6} \\
20 \\
\underline{-18} \\
2
\end{array}
$$

Ready to Go On?

LESSON 2 **Rational Numbers**

Skills Intervention: Multiplying Rational Numbers

When multiplying fractions, you multiply the numerators and the denominators.

The product of two numbers with the same sign is positive.
$(+) \cdot (+) = (+)$ or $(-) \cdot (-) = (+)$

The product of two numbers with different signs is negative.
$(+) \cdot (-) = (-)$ or $(-) \cdot (+) = (-)$

Multiplying a Fraction and an Integer

Multiply. Write the answer as a mixed number in simplest form.

$-5\left(2\dfrac{3}{4}\right)$

$= -5\left(\dfrac{\quad}{\quad}\right)$　　To change a mixed number to an improper fraction,

　　　　　　　　　　_____ the denominator by the whole number and

　　　　　　　　　　_____ the numerator.

$= -\dfrac{\quad}{\quad}$　　To multiply a fraction and integer, _____ the numerator

　　　　　　　　by the integer and _____ the denominator by _____.

$=$ _____　　Write the answer as a mixed number. Is the answer positive or

　　　　　　　negative? _____ How do you know? _____

　　　　　　　_____

Multiplying Fractions

Multiply. Write the answer in simplest form.

$\dfrac{-3}{5}\left(\dfrac{-2}{3}\right)$

$= \dfrac{-3 \cdot \quad}{\quad \cdot 3}$　　To multiply fractions, _____ the numerators and

　　　　　　　_____ the denominators.

$= \dfrac{(\quad)(-2)}{(5)(\quad)}$　　Cancel out the common factors.

$=$ _____　　Simplify. Is the answer positive or negative? _____

　　　　　　How do you know? _____

Ready to Go On?

LESSON
2

Rational Numbers

Problem Solving Intervention: Multiplying Rational Numbers

You can estimate to compare products of rational numbers. You can use fractions or decimals, whichever makes the comparison simpler.

Which product is greater, $-11.09 \cdot 0.247$ or $\frac{21}{99} \cdot \left(-15\frac{15}{16}\right)$?

Understand the Problem

1. Are you asked to find the exact products? What does the problem ask?

_____

2. Without calculating, what can you tell about the sign of both products?

_____

Make a Plan

3. What simple fraction is close to 0.247? _____

4. What simple decimal is close to $\frac{21}{99}$? _____

Solve

5. Round -11.09 and $-15\frac{15}{16}$ to the nearest integers.

_____

6. Write the two products with rounded factors. Which is greater?

_____

7. Without calculating either $-11.09 \cdot 0.247$ or $\frac{21}{99} \cdot \left(-15\frac{15}{16}\right)$, tell whether each product is greater than -3 or less than -3.

_____

8. Which product is greater, $-11.09 \cdot 0.247$ or $\frac{21}{99} \cdot \left(-15\frac{15}{16}\right)$? _____

Look Back

9. On the number line, show the approximate location of the two products.

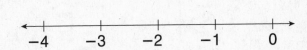

Holt McDougal Mathematics

Ready to Go On?

LESSON
3
Rational Numbers

Skills Intervention: Dividing Rational Numbers

To divide a number by a fraction multiply by the reciprocal. The **reciprocal** of a number is found by exchanging the numerator and denominator.

Number	**Reciprocal**	**Product**
$\frac{7}{8}$	$\frac{8}{7}$	$\frac{7}{8} \cdot \frac{8}{7} = 1$
-2, or $\frac{-2}{1}$	$\frac{1}{-2}$	$-2 \cdot \frac{1}{-2} = 1$

Dividing Fractions
Divide. Write each answer in simplest form.

A. $\frac{7}{18} \div \frac{1}{2}$

$\frac{7}{18} \div \frac{1}{2} = \frac{7}{18} \cdot \underline{} = \underline{}$ What is the reciprocal of $\frac{1}{2}$?

$= \frac{7 \cdot 2}{18 \cdot 1}$ How many times does 2 go into 18?

$= \underline{} = \underline{}$ Simplify.

B. $3\frac{1}{6} \div \frac{2}{3}$

$3\frac{1}{6} \div \frac{2}{3} = \underline{} \div \frac{2}{3}$ To write $3\frac{1}{6}$ as an improper fraction, multiply _____ by

_____ and add the numerator 1.

$\frac{19}{6} \div \frac{2}{3} = \frac{19}{6} \cdot \underline{}$ Multiply by the reciprocal of $\frac{2}{3}$.

$= \frac{19 \cdot 3}{6 \cdot 2}$ What is the common factor? _____

$= \frac{19}{4} = \underline{}$ Multiply and write as a mixed number.

© Houghton Mifflin Harcourt Publishing Company

Holt McDougal Mathematics

Name _____ Date _____ Class _____

Rational Numbers

Skills Intervention: Adding and Subtracting with Unlike Denominators

You can add or subtract fractions with unlike denominators by first finding a common denominator. There are two methods you can use to find the common denominator.

Method 1: Multiply one denominator by the other denominator.

Method 2: Find the **least common denominator (LCD)** by finding the least common multiple of the denominators.

Adding Fractions with Unlike Denominators

Add. $\frac{3}{5} + \frac{1}{7}$

To add two fractions, you need to have a _____.

Multiply 5×7 to get a common denominator of _____.

$= \frac{3}{5}\left(\underline{\hspace{1cm}}\right) + \frac{1}{7}\left(\underline{\hspace{1cm}}\right)$ Multiply by fractions equal to _____.

$= \underline{\hspace{1cm}} + \underline{\hspace{1cm}}$ Rewrite with common denominators.

$= \underline{\hspace{1cm}}$ Add the _____ and keep the

_____ the same.

Evaluating Expressions with Rational Numbers

Evaluate $n - \frac{3}{5}$ for $n = -\frac{1}{7}$.

$n - \frac{3}{5}$

$= \frac{\overline{}}{\underline{}} - \frac{3}{5}$ Substitute _____ for n.

$= \left(-\frac{1}{7}\right)\left(\frac{\overline{}}{\underline{}}\right) - \frac{3}{5}\left(\frac{\overline{}}{\underline{}}\right)$ Multiply by fractions equal to _____.

$= -\frac{5}{\underline{}} - \frac{21}{\underline{}}$ Rewrite with a common denominator.

$= \frac{\overline{}}{35}$ Subtract. Is the answer positive or negative?

_____

Holt McDougal Mathematics

Ready to Go On?

Rational Numbers

SECTION A: Quiz for Lessons 1 Through 4

1 Rational Numbers
Simplify.

1. $\frac{10}{24}$ _____

2. $\frac{21}{48}$ _____

3. $\frac{22}{77}$ _____

4. $\frac{13}{117}$ _____

2 Multiplying Rational Numbers
Multiply. Write each answer in simplest form.

5. $2\left(3\frac{3}{4}\right)$

6. $-3\frac{2}{5}\left(1\frac{7}{10}\right)$

7. $-4\frac{3}{5}\left(-3\frac{1}{7}\right)$

8. $\frac{8}{35}\left(-5\frac{4}{9}\right)$

_____ _____ _____ _____

9. Devon is making 8 loaves of bread. Each loaf of
bread needs $3\frac{3}{4}$ cups of flour. How much flour does
Devon need to make the bread?   _____

3 Dividing Rational Numbers
Divide. Write each answer in simplest form.

10. $\frac{4}{5} \div \frac{7}{10}$

11. $3.2 \div 0.8$

12. $-\frac{5}{11} \div 3$

13. $45.62 \div 0.02$

_____ _____ _____ _____

4 Adding and Subtracting with Unlike Denominators
Add or subtract.

14. $\frac{3}{5} + \frac{1}{4}$

15. $2\frac{3}{7} - 1\frac{1}{2}$

16. $\frac{22}{9} + 3\frac{5}{6}$

17. $7\frac{2}{5} - 4\frac{1}{3}$

_____ _____ _____ _____

18. $1\frac{7}{10} + 2\frac{1}{8}$

19. $3\frac{8}{9} - \frac{2}{3}$

20. $3\frac{5}{8} + \frac{1}{2}$

21. $2\frac{7}{8} - \frac{2}{3}$

_____ _____ _____ _____

Holt McDougal Mathematics

Ready to Go On?

Rational Numbers

Section A Enrichment: Guess the Operation

If you are given a problem without the operation symbol, you can use number sense to help you figure out what operation was used.

A. $\frac{1}{2}$ ☐ $\frac{1}{3}$ = $1\frac{1}{2}$

The answer is _____ than the first number.

The second number is _____.

So, it is not subtraction because the answer would have to be _____ than the first number.

What is $1\frac{1}{2}$ as an improper fraction? _____

What is the reciprocal of the second number? _____

What operation uses reciprocals? _____

$\frac{1}{2}$ ☐ $\frac{1}{3}$ = $1\frac{1}{2}$

B. 0.08 ☐ 0.007 = 0.00056

The answer is _____ than the first number.

The second number is _____.

So, it is not addition because the sum of two positives is _____ than either number.

How many decimal places are in the answer? _____

How many in the first number? _____ The second? _____

What operation has you add the number of decimal places in each number?

_____

0.08 ☐ 0.007 = 0.00056

Use number sense to figure out what operation is being performed in each problem.

1. 0.25 ☐ 0.5 = −0.25

2. 1.5 ☐ 0.3 = 5

3. 0.7 ☐ 0.9 = 1.6

4. 2.7 ☐ 1.11 = 2.997

5. $\frac{2}{5}$ ☐ $\frac{8}{5}$ = 2

6. $\frac{2}{3}$ ☐ $\frac{1}{4}$ = $\frac{1}{6}$

7. $\frac{3}{8}$ ☐ $\frac{1}{2}$ = $\frac{3}{4}$

8. $\frac{9}{10}$ ☐ $\frac{2}{5}$ = $\frac{1}{2}$

9. −0.6 ☐ 0.95 = 0.35

10. $\frac{4}{7}$ ☐ $\frac{3}{4}$ = $\frac{16}{21}$

11. $\frac{7}{8}$ ☐ $\frac{1}{4}$ = $\frac{5}{8}$

12. 0.06 ☐ 0.03 = 0.0018

Holt McDougal Mathematics

Name _____ Date _____ Class _____

Rational Numbers
Skills Intervention: Solving Equations with Rational Numbers

You solve an equation by isolating the variable. Use inverse operations to isolate the variable.

Solving Equations with Decimals
Solve.

A. $w - 6.5 = 31$

_____ _____   What number should you add to both sides?

$w =$ _____   What does w equal?

B. $\frac{x}{4.6} = 8$

$\frac{x}{4.6} \cdot$ _____ $= 8 \cdot ($_____$)$ To isolate x, multiply both sides of the equation by

_____.

$x =$ _____   What does x equal?

What can you do to check your answer? _____

_____

C. $-3.7x = 22.2$

$\dfrac{-3.7}{\underline{}}x = \dfrac{22.2}{\underline{}}$ What number should you divide both sides of the equation by?

$x =$ _____   What does x equal? Does the solution check?

Solving Equations with Fractions
Solve.

$x + \frac{3}{5} = \frac{6}{7}$

$x + \frac{3}{5} -$ _____ $= \frac{6}{7} -$ _____   What number should you subtract from both sides of the equation?

$x = \frac{6}{7} - \frac{3}{5}$ To subtract fractions you must first find

_____.

$x = \dfrac{30}{\underline{}} - \dfrac{21}{\underline{}}$ What is the common denominator?

$x =$ _____   What does x equal? Does the solution check?

Holt McDougal Mathematics

Ready to Go On?

LESSON 5

Rational Numbers

Problem Solving Intervention: Solving Equations with Rational Numbers

You can use equations with rational numbers to model situations and solve problems.

Kim worked from 3:30 P.M. to 7:15 P.M. on Friday and from 8:45 A.M. to 1:30 P.M. on Saturday. She earned $55.25 for the two days. How much did she earn per hour?

Understand the Problem

1. Do you have enough information to figure out how many hours Kim worked?

_____

2. What are you trying to find out?

_____

Make a Plan

3. Let t stand for the total number of hours Kim worked on Friday and Saturday. If you know that she earned $55.25, what equation can you use to find r, her hourly rate?

_____

Solve

4. How many hours did Kim work on Friday? On Saturday? On both days together?

_____

5. Find Kim's hourly rate r by solving the equation you wrote for Exercise 3. (*Hint:* Use the value of t you found in Exercise 4.)

_____

Look Back

6. Use the value you found for r and see if Kim earned $55.25.

_____

Holt McDougal Mathematics

Name _____ Date _____ Class _____

LESSON 6

Rational Numbers

Skills Intervention: Solving Two-Step Equations

You solve an equation by isolating the variable. To isolate the variable, you may have to use more than one operation.

Solving Two-Step Equations

Solve.

A. $\dfrac{a}{3} + 7 = 15$

$\dfrac{a}{3} + 7 = 15$ What is the opposite of adding 7? _____

$\dfrac{\underline{\quad}}{\quad} \quad \underline{\quad}$

$\dfrac{a}{3} = \underline{\quad}$ Simplify.

$\underline{\quad} \cdot \dfrac{a}{3} = 8 \cdot \underline{\quad}$ To undo division, multiply both sides of the equation by ___.

$a = \underline{\quad}$ Solve for a.

Check:

$\dfrac{a}{3} + 7 = 15$

$\dfrac{\overline{\quad}}{3} + 7 \overset{?}{=} 15$ What value do you substitute into the equation for a? _____

$\underline{\quad} + 7 \overset{?}{=} 15$ Does the solution check? _____

B. $-13.6 = -3.5f - 4.5$

$-13.6 = -3.5f - 4.5$ How do you undo -4.5? _____

$\dfrac{\underline{\quad}}{\quad} \qquad \dfrac{\underline{\quad}}{\quad}$

$-9.1 = -3.5f$ How do you isolate f?

$\dfrac{-9.1}{\underline{\quad}} = \dfrac{-3.5f}{\underline{\quad}}$ _____

$\underline{\quad} = f$ Solve for f. Does the solution check? _____

C. $\dfrac{w + 7}{8} = 11$

     To isolate the variable, how do you clear the fraction?

$\underline{\quad} \cdot \dfrac{w + 7}{8} = 11 \cdot \underline{\quad}$ _____

$w + 7 = \underline{\quad}$ To isolate w, what is the next step?

$\dfrac{\underline{\quad}}{\quad} \qquad \dfrac{\underline{\quad}}{\quad}$ _____

$w = \underline{\quad}$ Solve for w. How do you check the solution?

_____

_____

LESSON 6

Ready to Go On?
Rational Numbers
Problem Solving Intervention: Solving Two-Step Equations

You can write equations to help solve some problems involving plane figures.

A farmer plans to build a square chicken pen from the 114 yards of fencing she has. She needs to save 20 feet of the fencing for another project. What is the longest that each side of the chicken pen can be?

Understand the Problem

1. Complete to show what you know and what you need to find.

    There are _____ yards of fencing in all. The farmer can use all but _____ feet.

    The shape of the pen is _____. Find _____.

Make a Plan

2. Why does it make sense to convert 114 yards to feet?

    _____

3. Complete the equation to show how the quantities in the problem are related. Use *s* for the longest length in feet of each side of the pen.

    _____ + _____ = 3 • _____

Solve

4. Solve the equation you wrote in Exercise 3.

    _____

5. What is the longest that each side of the chicken pen can be?

    _____

Look Back

6. Use your answer to calculate how much fencing is used for the pen and the other project. See if you get 114 yards.

    _____

    _____

SECTION 1B **Rational Numbers**

SECTION B: Quiz for Lessons 5 Through 6

5 Solving Equations with Rational Numbers

Solve.

1. $x - 3.5 = 1.2$

2. $y + \dfrac{4}{5} = \dfrac{2}{8}$

3. $2t = -5.7$

_____

4. $\dfrac{9}{24}h = -\dfrac{36}{8}$

5. $-9 = \dfrac{m}{2.7}$

6. $k - \dfrac{3}{8} = \dfrac{13}{22}$

_____

7. $\dfrac{s}{5.3} = 2.6$

8. $4.5 + p = -6.4$

9. $\dfrac{12}{15} = w - \dfrac{3}{5}$

_____

10. Joe just moved into his new apartment. It takes him $5\dfrac{1}{4}$ hours to paint one bedroom. His apartment has 4 bedrooms. How many hours will Joe need to paint all the bedrooms of his new apartment?

_____

11. Katie and Ann are going to make cornbread for the bake sale at school. The recipe calls for $2\dfrac{3}{4}$ cups of cornmeal for 1 loaf of cornbread. How many cups of cornmeal will they need to make 12 loaves of cornbread?

_____

12. A bag of dried cherries had 387.9 total calories. There are 4.5 servings per bag. How many calories are in each serving of dried cherries?

_____

Holt McDougal Mathematics

Ready to Go On?

SECTION 1B **Rational Numbers**

SECTION B: Quiz for Lessons 5 Through 6, continued

6 Solving Two-Step Equations

Solve.

13. $4w - 7.5 = 2.7$

14. $\dfrac{x - 2}{4} = -3.75$

15. $5t + 5.7 = 9.2$

_____

_____

_____

16. $\dfrac{s + 8}{25} = -\dfrac{12}{5}$

17. $-11 = \dfrac{m}{0.3} - 18.3$

18. $8h - \dfrac{6}{7} = \dfrac{2}{3}$

_____

_____

_____

19. $65.3 - \dfrac{k}{12.7} = 25.3$

20. $6.9 + 8p = -12.3$

21. $\dfrac{11}{15} = \dfrac{8}{35}y + \dfrac{3}{7}$

_____

_____

_____

22. Judy sells stamps for her grandmother. She earns $27 per week, plus $2.25 for each stamp that she sells. Last week, Judy earned $60.75. How many stamps did Judy sell that week?

_____

23. The local ice skating rink charges $8 for admission. Skate rental costs $5.50 per pair. On Friday night, skate rentals brought in $341. The rink made $1,333 that night. How many people went to the skating rink Friday night?

_____

24. A digital cable company charges $56.65 per month for cable and high-speed Internet service. The cable company charges $0.11 for each minute. A family's cable bill was $128.37 last month. How many total minutes did the family use high-speed Internet?

_____

Ready to Go On?

| SECTION | **Rational Numbers** |
| 1B | Section B Enrichment: Combining Like Terms |

When an equation has multiple terms that include a variable, you must get all the terms with variables on one side of the equation and all the numbers on the other side.

$$8x + 5 = 6x - 7$$ First, get all the numbers on one side of the equation.
$$\underline{-5 \qquad -5}$$ Subtract 5 from both sides.
$$8x = 6x - 12$$

$$\underline{-6x \quad -6x}$$ Now subtract $6x$ from both sides.
$$2x = -12$$ Divide both sides by 2.
$$x = -6$$

$$8(-6) + 5 = 6(-6) - 7$$ Check your answer by substituting the x-value into the original equation.
$$-48 + 5 = -36 - 7$$ Simplify.
$$-43 = -43$$ The equation is true when $x = -6$.

Simplify each equation so that all the variables are on one side.

1. $7x + 4 = 2x - 8$ _____

2. $2a + 6 = 3a + 2$ _____

3. $6f - 3 = 12f + 4$ _____

4. $4t + 9 = 6t + 7$ _____

5. $3m - 2 = 4m + 1$ _____

6. $8r - 4 = 12r + 6$ _____

7. $5j + 2 = 4j - 7$ _____

8. $6w + 3 = 2w - 8$ _____

Solve.

9. $3y + 5 = 4y + 8$ _____

10. $4b - 1 = -3b + 6$ _____

11. $5g - 4 = 3g + 9$ _____

12. $2s + 3 = 8s - 2$ _____

13. $2m - 2 = 4m + 1$ _____

14. $3s + 6 = s - 2$ _____

15. $3k - 10 = 7k + 3$

16. $10z + 5 = 7z - 9$

_____

_____

Ready to Go On?

LESSON	**Graphs and Functions**
1	**Skills Intervention: Ordered Pairs**

An **ordered pair** is one way to express a solution to an equation.

Deciding Whether an Ordered Pair Is a Solution of an Equation

Determine whether this ordered pair is a solution of $y = 6x - 4$.

$(3, 14)$ $y = 6x - 4$ What number do you substitute for x?

$\underline{} \overset{?}{=} 6(\underline{}) - 4$ What number do you substitute for y?

$\underline{} \overset{?}{=} \underline{}$ Evaluate the right side of the equation.

Is (3, 14) a solution of the equation? Why? _____

Creating a Table of Ordered Pair Solutions

Use the given values to make a table of solutions. $y = 2x + 2$ for $x = 0, 1, 2, 3$

Substitute each value of x into the equation. Fill in the missing values to complete the table.

x	$2x + 2$	y	(x, y)
0	$2(0) + 2$	2	$(0, 2)$
1	$2(\_) + 2$	_	$(1, \_)$
2	$2(\_) + 2$	_	$(\_, \_)$
3	$2(\_) + 2$	_	$(\_, \_)$

Recreation Application

When renting a bike at City Park, Joe must first pay a deposit and then pay a charge per hour. If the per hour fee is \$5 and the deposit is \$15, then the cost c of renting the bike for h hours can be determined using the equation: $c = 5h + 15$.

A. How much will it cost Joe to rent the bike for 4 hours?

$c = 5h + 15$

$c = 5(\underline{}) + 15$ What number do you substitute for h?

$c = \underline{}$ Evaluate.

It will cost Joe \$____ to rent the bike for 4 hours.

The solution can be written as (4, ____).

B. How much will it cost Joe to rent the bike for 6 hours?

$c = 5h + 15$

$c = 5(\underline{}) + 15$ What number do you substitute for h?

$c = \underline{}$ Evaluate.

It will cost Joe \$____ to rent the bike for 6 hours.

The solution can be written as _____.

     Holt McDougal Mathematics

Name _____ Date _____ Class _____

LESSON
1

Graphs and Functions

Problem Solving Intervention: Ordered Pairs

When you use an equation to solve a problem, you can often use ordered pairs to show the solution.

The first story of a new skyscraper will be 25 feet high. Each of the other stories will be 12 feet high. The tower at the top will be 25 feet tall. If the building can be no taller than 800 feet, how many stories can there be?

Understand the Problem

1. What are the requirements for the skyscraper?

_____

_____

Make a Plan

2. If you write an equation relating all the given information, what variables will you use and what will they stand for?

_____

_____

3. What value will you set h equal to? _____

Solve

4. Using n to stand for the number of stories above the first, write an expression for the height of all the stories above the first. _____

5. Write an equation relating h, the maximum height in feet of the skyscraper, to the height of the three sections you listed in question 1.

_____

6. Solve the equation if $h = 800$, the maximum height allowed.

_____

Look Back

7. If n is 62.5, how many stories can there be? Explain.

_____

_____

8. Solve the equation for $n = 62$ and show the solution as an ordered pair. _____

Holt McDougal Mathematics

Ready to Go On?

LESSON 2

Graphs and Functions

Skills Intervention: Graphing on a Coordinate Plane

A **coordinate plane** contains a horizontal number line called the **x-axis** and a vertical number line called the **y-axis**. The axes divide the coordinate plane into four **quadrants**. The point where the two axes intersect is the **origin**. The **x-coordinate** indicates movement left or right, and the **y-coordinate** indicates movement up or down.

Vocabulary
coordinate plane
x-axis
y-axis
quadrant
origin
x-coordinate
y-coordinate

Finding the Coordinates and Quadrants of Points on a Plane
Give the coordinates of each point.

A. point E

Is the point left or right of the origin? _____

How many spaces? ____

Is the x-coordinate positive or negative? _____

Is the point above or below the origin? _____

How many spaces? ____

Is the y-coordinate positive or negative? _____

What are the coordinates of point E? _____ What quadrant is it in? ____

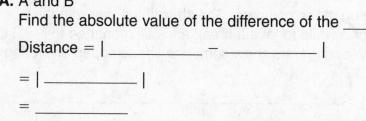

B. point F   The point is _____ of the origin ____ spaces. The sign is _____.

The point is how many units below the origin? _____

What are the coordinates of the point? _____ What quadrant is it in? ____

Finding Horizontal and Vertical Distances
Find the distance between the two points.

A. A and B

Find the absolute value of the difference of the _____ -coordinates.

Distance = | _____ − _____ |

= | _____ |

= _____

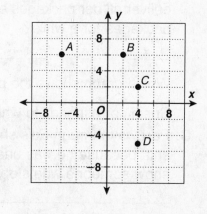

B. C and D

Find the absolute value of the difference of the

_____ -coordinates.

Distance = | _____ − _____ |

= | _____ |

= _____

Holt McDougal Mathematics

Name _____ Date _____ Class _____

Graphs and Functions

LESSON 3

Skills Intervention: Interpreting Graphs

You can relate both **continuous graphs**, like the ones below, and **discrete graphs**, made of unconnected points, to given descriptions by identifying key words in the descriptions.

<table>
<tr><td>Vocabulary</td></tr>
<tr><td>continuous graph
discrete graph</td></tr>
</table>

Matching Situations to Graphs

Marcy, Susie, and Ed all work at a package delivery company. The graphs below show the packages each person had left to deliver during the shift. Tell which person corresponds to which situation.

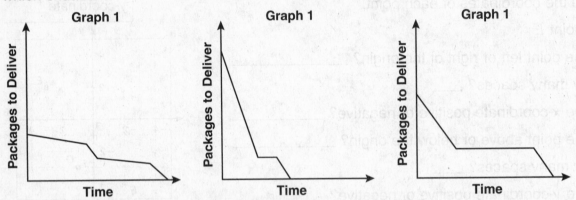

A. Marcy is new on the job. It took her nearly her entire shift to deliver all her packages, and she was given the least number of packages to deliver at the start of the day. Which graphs show someone who took almost the entire shift to deliver the packages?

_____

Which graph shows the person who starts with the least number of packages?

_____

Marcy corresponds to which graph? _____

B. Susie is the faster delivery person at the company. She started the day with the most packages. She stopped for a while to take a break and still managed to deliver all her packages early. Which graphs show someone who stopped delivering packages for a while?

_____

Which graph shows the person who finished early? _____

Susie corresponds to which graph? _____

C. Part way through Ed's shift, his delivery van broke down. He finished late in the shift because he was unable to deliver packages for half the day. Which graphs show someone who stopped delivering packages for half the day?

_____

Ed corresponds to which graph? _____

Holt McDougal Mathematics

SECTION 2A

Ready to Go On?

Graphs and Functions

SECTION A: Quiz for Lessons 1 Through 3

1 Ordered Pairs

Determine whether each ordered pair is a solution of $y = 3x - 4$.

1. (12, 32) _____

2. (−4, 8) _____

3. (1.4, 0.2) _____

4. (1.5, 1.5) _____

Acme Auto Rental charges $22.50 per day plus $0.15 per mile to rent a compact car. The equation for the total cost c of the car, including mileage, is $c = 22.5 + 0.15m$, where m is the number of miles driven. Calculate the total cost to rent the car for each of the number of miles driven.

5. $m = 80$ miles _____

6. $m = 300$ miles _____

7. $m = 240$ miles _____

8. $m = 148$ miles _____

9. The Total Design T-Shirt Company has a one-time charge of $32.00 for a design and an additional $3.00 to print the design on each t-shirt. Let t represent the number of t-shirts and c represent the total cost. Write an equation that can be used to find the total cost to pick a design and have it printed on t t-shirts. _____

2 Graphing on a Coordinate Plane

Give the coordinates and quadrant number of each point.

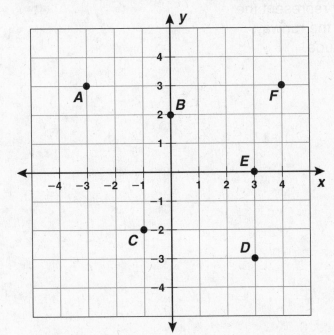

10. A _____

11. B _____

12. C _____

13. D _____

14. E _____

15. F _____

Ready to Go On?

Graphs and Functions

SECTION A: Quiz for Lessons 1 Through 3, continued

3 Interpreting Graphs

Tell which graph corresponds to each situation below.

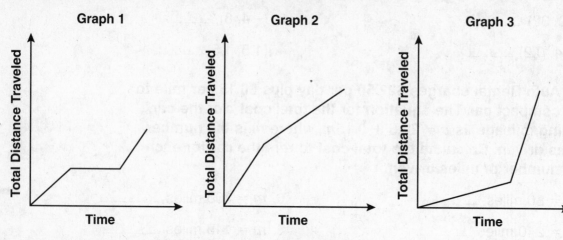

Graph 1 **Graph 2** **Graph 3**

16. Rosita walks from her home to town and then rides with a friend in her car to the other side of town.

_____

17. Reynaldo rides his bicycle from his home to the beginning of a path where he leaves his bike and takes a walking trip along a river.

_____

18. Simon rides his bicycle to the market where he stops to buy some snacks. He then continues on his bicycle at the same pace to his grandmother's house.

_____

19. Create a graph that would most likely represent the speed of an airplane as it taxis down the runway, takes off and reaches its cruising altitude.

Holt McDougal Mathematics

Ready to Go On?

SECTION 2A Graphs and Functions

Section A Enrichment: Coordinate Plane Puzzles

Fill in the letter that names each point for the given coordinates to complete the riddle.

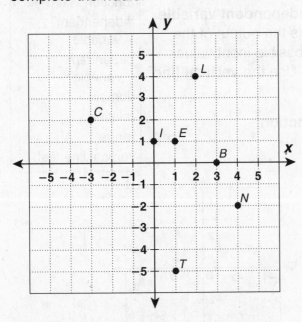

What did the zero say to the eight?

___ ___ ___ ___ ___ ___ ___ ___
(4, −2) (0, 1) (−3, 2) (1, 1) (3, 0) (1, 1) (2, 4) (1, −5)

Plot the points below. Then, connect them in the order they are listed and name the shape you form.

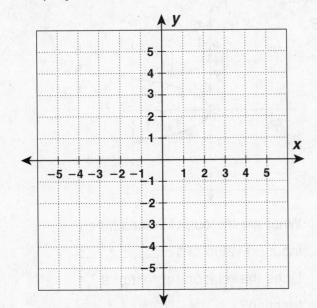

1. (0, 4)

2. (1, 2)

3. (3, 2)

4. (1, 0)

5. (3, −3)

6. (0, −1)

7. (−3, −3)

8. (−1, 0)

9. (−3, 2)

10. (−1, 2)

_____

Holt McDougal Mathematics

LESSON 4

Graphs and Functions

Skills Intervention: Functions

A **function** is a rule that relates two quantities so that each input or *x*-value gives only one output or *y*-value. When a function is written as an equation in two variables, the **independent variable** is the input and the **dependent variable** is the output of the function. The **domain** of a **relation** is all its possible input values and its **range** is all its possible output values. Use the **vertical line test** to test whether a graph is a function.

Finding Different Representations of a Function

Make a table and graph of $y = x^2 - 1$.

Complete the table and then plot each point.

x	$x^2 - 1$	y	(x, y)
−2	$(-2)^2 - 1$	3	(−2, 3)
−1	$(\_\_)^2 - 1$		( )
0	$(\_\_)^2 - 1$		( )
1	$(\_\_)^2 - 1$		( )
2	$(\_\_)^2 - 1$		( )

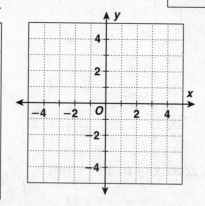

Connect the points with a smooth curve.

Does each input value have one output value? _____

Identifying Functions

Determine if each relation represents a function.

A.

x	y
2	4
6	8
10	12
14	16

B.

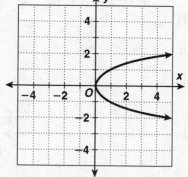

Does each input (*x*) have only one output (*y*)? _____

Does the relation represent a function? _____

What are the output values for an input (*x*) value of 1? _____

Does the relation represent a function? _____

Holt McDougal Mathematics

| LESSON 5 | # Graphs and Functions |

Skills Intervention: Equations, Tables, and Graphs

You can use an equation to represent data in different ways.

Using Equations to Generate Different Representations of Data

The distance a car has traveled is represented by the equation $d = 45h$, where d is the distance traveled and h is the number of hours. Make a table and a graph of the equation.

h	$45h$	d
0	45(0)	0
1	45(__)	____
2	45(__)	____
3	45(__)	____

To find d, multiply h by 45.

What is the distance after 0 hours? _____

After 1 hour? _____ After 3 hours? _____

Complete the table.

Use the information in the table to make a graph.

h represents the _____ and d represents the _____.

What is the x-coordinate of the first point? _____

What is the y-coordinate of the first point? _____

Make the graph.

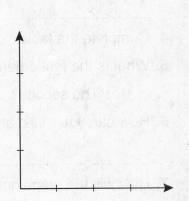

Using Tables to Generate Different Representations of Data

Use the table to make a graph and write an equation.

x	2	4	6	8
y	1	2	3	4

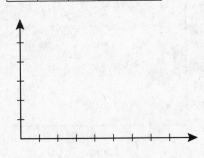

Use the data in the graph to plot points on the graph.

What are the coordinates of the first point? (_____)

Complete the graph.
Look for a pattern in the values.

2 _____ = 1   4 _____ = 2

6 _____ = 3   8 _____ = 4

Each value of x is _____ to get each value of y.

Write the equation. _____

Ready to Go On?

LESSON
5

Graphs and Functions
Problem Solving Intervention: Equations, Tables, and Graphs

You can make a table and a graph to answer a word problem.

The amount of calories burned by swimming laps is represented by the equation $c = 12s$ where c is the number of calories and s is the number of laps. Use a table and a graph to find out how many calories Matilda burns when she swims 8 laps.

Understand the Problem

1. What quantity are you asked to find? _____

2. What do we know? _____

Make a Plan

3. How can a table help?

   _____

4. Complete the table.

5. What is the first ordered pair from the table?

   _____ The second? _____

6. How can you make a graph from the data in the table?

   _____

7. How will the graph help you answer the question?

   _____

s	$12s$	c
1	12(1)	12
2	12(2)	____
3	12(__)	____
4	12(__)	____

Solve

8. Make a graph for the data in the table.

9. Extend the graph. What is the value of c

   when $s = 8$? ____

10. Answer the question.

    _____

Look Back

11. How can you show that your answer is reasonable?

_____

Ready to Go On?

SECTION 2B # Graphs and Functions

SECTION B: Quiz for Lessons 4 Through 5

4 Functions

Make a table and a graph for the function.

1. $y = 3x - 2$

x	$3x - 2$	y
-2	$3(\underline{}) - 2$	___
-1	$3(\underline{}) - 2$	___
0	$3(\underline{}) - 2$	___
1	$3(\underline{}) - 2$	___
2	$3(\underline{}) - 2$	___

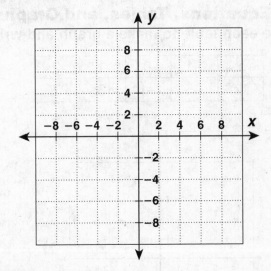

Determine if each relation represents a function.

2.

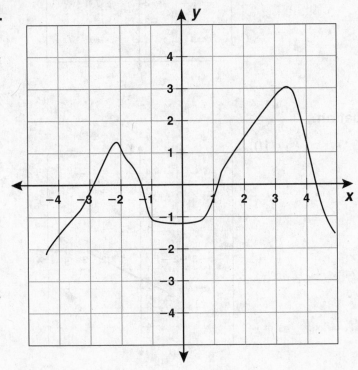

_____

3.

x	1	2	3	4
y	8	12	15	16

4.

x	5	6	5	7
y	8	11	14	17

_____

_____

5. $y = x^2 + 2$ _____

6. $y = 3x + 2$ _____

Holt McDougal Mathematics

Name _____ Date _____ Class _____

5 Equations, Tables, and Graphs

Use each table to make a graph and write an equation.

7.

x	−1	0	1	2
y	−5	−1	3	7

_____

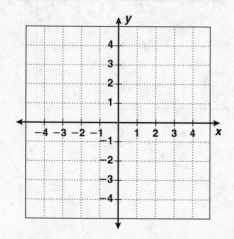

8.

x	−3	−2	−1	0
y	−3	−1	1	3

_____

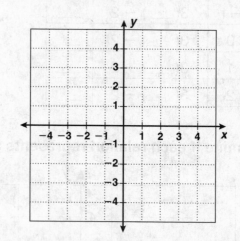

Use each graph to write an equation.

9.

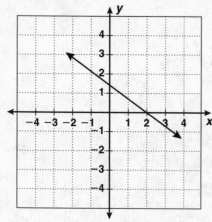

_____

10.

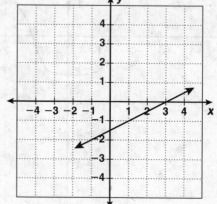

_____

Ready to Go On?

SECTION
2B
Graphs and Functions

Section B Enrichment: Using a Graph to Solve Word Problems

You can use a graph to help you answer word problems. Look at the graph below.

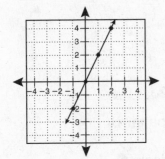

Does it show a positive or negative relationship? _____

For every unit to the right, how much does the line rise?

_____

This amount of vertical change divided by the amount of horizontal change is called slope. It tells you what the variable in the equation of the line is multiplied by.

When $x = 0$, what does y equal? _____

This means that there is no number added to the variable in the equation of the line.

What is the equation of this line? _____

Jaqueline made this graph of her rate for doing yard work. Answer the questions below based on her graph.

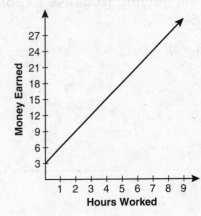

1. Jaqueline has an initial charge to cover supplies

   for each client. What is it? _____

2. What is Jaqueline's hourly rate? _____

3. Write an equation to describe Jaqueline's rate. Use h
   for the number of hours and t for the total amount of

   money she makes. _____

4. Explain why the number multiplied by the variable is not 1, even
   though the graph looks like the line rises at a 1 to 1 ratio.

   _____

   _____

5. Jaqueline spent 2 hours weeding Mrs. Olsen's garden.
   Use the equation from Exercise 3 to find her pay.   _____

6. Jaqueline spent 3 hours working in her mother's yard.
   As a familiy discount, she took off the supply charge.
   How much did Jaqueline earn from her mother?   _____

7. Saturday, Jaqueline spent 2 hours mowing Mr. Harrison's

   lawn. Then she spent 1 hour pruning Mrs. Peterson's

   shrubs. Finally, she spent $1\frac{1}{2}$ hours raking leaves at

   Miss Ryder's house. How much did Jaqueline make

   on Saturday? (Each get a supply charge.)   _____

Holt McDougal Mathematics

Name _____ Date _____ Class _____

LESSON
1

Exponents and Roots

Skills Intervention: Integer Exponents

A number raised to a negative exponent equals one divided by that
number raised to the opposite of the exponent.

Using a Pattern to Simplify Negative Exponents
Simplify. Write in decimal form.

10^{-2} Is the exponent positive or negative? _____

$10^{-2} = \dfrac{1}{\rule{2cm}{0.4pt}}$ Write the reciprocal and extend the pattern.

$10^{-2} = \dfrac{1}{\rule{1cm}{0.4pt}} = \rule{1cm}{0.4pt}$ Simplify and write the fraction as a decimal.

Simplifying Negative Exponents
Simplify.

$(-3)^{-5}$ What is the exponent? _____

                   When an exponent is negative, write the reciprocal.

_____   What is the sign of the exponent, now? _____

_____   Write the product of $\rule{0.5cm}{0.4pt} \cdot \dfrac{1}{-3}$.

                   Simplify.

_____

Using the Order of Operations
Simplify.

$4 - 5^0 + (7 - 5)^{-4}$

$4 - 5^0 + (\underline{\hspace{0.7cm}})^{-4}$ What operation do you do first?

             _____

             What operation do you do next? _____

$4 - \underline{\hspace{0.7cm}} + \dfrac{}{\underline{\hspace{0.7cm}}}$ A number with 0 as an exponent equals ___.

             To change the sign of an exponent, write the _____.

$4 - \underline{\hspace{0.7cm}} + \underline{\hspace{0.7cm}}$ Simplify.

             _____ and _____ from left to right.

_____

          Holt McDougal Mathematics

LESSON 2

Exponents and Roots

Skills Intervention: Properties of Exponents

Factors of a power can be grouped in different ways giving the same product. When the powers have the same base, keep these rules in mind:

Multiply: add exponents   Divide: subtract exponents

Multiplying Powers with the Same Base

Multiply. Write the product as one power.

A. $6^4 \cdot 6^7$ Are the bases the same? _____

6——   What do you do to the exponents when multiplying? _____

6—   Does the base change? _____ What is the exponent? _____

B. $t \cdot t^8$ Are the bases the same? _____

$t^- \cdot t^8$ What is the exponent of the first t? _____

t——   To multiply powers with the same base, what do you do

          with the exponents? _____

____   What is the exponent? _____

Dividing Powers with the Same Base

Divide. Write the quotient as one power.

$\dfrac{10^{12}}{10^9}$ Are the bases the same? _____

10——   What do you do to the exponents when dividing? _____

____   What is the base? _____ What is the exponent? _____

When a power is raised to a power, multiply the exponents.

Raising a Power to a Power

Simplify.

A. $(6^3)^4$

6——   What do you do to the exponents? _____

6—   What power is 6 raised to? _____

B. $(9^5)^{-2}$

9 What do you do to the exponents? _____

9——   What power is 9 raised to? _____

Ready to Go On?

LESSON	# Exponents and Roots
2	**Problem Solving Intervention: Properties of Exponents**

You can use exponents to work with very large numbers—even in your head.

It takes sunlight about 8 minutes to reach Earth. Light travels at about 186,000 miles per second. Earth is about 93 million miles from the sun. Is 8 minutes a reasonable figure?

Understand the Problem

1. How are distance, speed, and time related?

   _____

   _____

2. How can you figure out how far something travels if
   you know its speed and how long it travels?   _____

Make a Plan

3. Why might you use powers of ten to help solve this problem?

   _____

   _____

   _____

Solve

4. The speed of light in mi/sec is closest to what power of ten?   _____

5. How many seconds are there in 8 minutes?   _____

6. Since you rounded down the speed of light, you can round
   up the time. What is your answer to Exercise 5 rounded up
   to the next highest power of ten?   _____

7. Use properties of exponents to multiply the speed of light (Exercise 4) by the time
   in seconds it takes to reach Earth (Exercise 6). What did you just calculate?

   _____

Look Back

8. Make sure you answer the question being asked.

   _____

   _____

Holt McDougal Mathematics

Ready to Go On?

LESSON	**Exponents and Roots**
3	**Skills Intervention: Scientific Notation**

A shorthand way of writing large numbers as the product of a
number and a power of ten is known as **scientific notation.**

Translating Scientific Notation to Standard Notation
Write each number in standard notation.

A. 3.72×10^6

3.72×10^6 Is the exponent on 10 positive or negative? _____

$3.72 \times$ _____ 10^6 has ____ zeroes.

_____   Move the decimal point ____ places to the _____.

B. 2.46×10^{-3}

2.46×10^{-3} Is the exponent on 10 positive or negative? _____

$2.46 \times$ _____   What does 10^{-3} equal?

$2.46 \div$ _____   Divide by the reciprocal.

_____   Move the decimal point ____ places to the _____.

C. -8.9×10^5

-8.9×10^5 Is the exponent on 10 positive or negative? _____

$-8.9 \times$ _____ 10^5 has ____ zeroes.

_____   Move the decimal point ____ places to the _____.

Translating Standard Notation to Scientific Notation
Write 0.0000378 in scientific notation.

0.0000378

3.78   How many places do you move the decimal point to get a

                   number between 1 and 10? ____

$3.78 \times$ ____$^?$ Set up scientific notation.
                   The decimal point needs to be moved which direction to

                   change 3.78 to 0.0000378? _____

                   Will the exponent be positive or negative? _____

3.78×10—   What is the exponent?

Check: Does $3.78 \times 10^{-5} = 3.78 \times 0.00001 = 0.0000378$? _____

         Holt McDougal Mathematics

Ready to Go On?

LESSON **3**

Exponents and Roots

Problem Solving Intervention: Scientific Notation

You can use scientific notation to make it easier to compare and order very small numbers.

Put the speeds in the table in order from fastest to slowest.

Event	Speed
Fingernail growth	3×10^{-4} cm/h
Growth of some lichen	10^{-10} km/h
Garden snail crawling	8×10^{-3} km/h

Understand the Problem

1. Can you conclude that fingernail growth is faster than lichen growth just because $3 \times 10^{-4} > 10^{-10}$? Explain.

_____

_____

Make a Plan

2. Fill in the blanks with a power of ten to convert centimeters to kilometers and then centimeters per hour to kilometers per hour.

1 cm = _____ m ⟶ 1 m = _____ km

So, 1 cm = _____ • _____, or _____ km

3×10^{-4} cm/h = 3×10^{-4} cm/h • _____ km/cm = $3 \times$ _____ km/h

Solve

3. Which is faster, $3 • 10^{-9}$ km/h or $1 • 10^{-10}$ km/h? _____

4. Which is faster, $8 • 10^{-3}$ km/h or $1 • 10^{-10}$ km/h? _____

5. List the 3 speeds in order from fastest to slowest.

_____

_____

Look Back

6. Why does it make sense that when you convert from centimeters per hour to kilometers per hour, you get a smaller number?

_____

_____

Holt McDougal Mathematics

Ready to Go On?

Exponents and Roots

Skills Intervention: Operating with Scientific Notation

Division with Scientific Notation

The mass of Saturn is 5.69×10^{26}. The mass of Mars is 6.42×10^{23}. About how many times greater is the mass of Saturn than the mass of Mars? Write your answer in scientific notation.

Mass of Saturn
Mass of Mars   _____

Write the ratio of the masses. _____

_____

Write as a product of two fractions. _____

Divide the coefficients. Subtract the exponents. _____

Write the result in scientific notation. _____

The mass of Saturn is _____ greater than the mass of Mars.

Multiplication with Scientific Notation

The radius of the Sun is about 1.75×10^2 times greater than the radius of Earth. The Earth's radius is about 3.95×10^6. What is the radius of Sun written in scientific notation?

$$\frac{\text{radius of Sun}}{3.95 \times 10^6} = 1.75 \times 10^2$$

Solve for the radius of the Sun.

When you cross multiply, what you quantities do you multiply?

(_____)(_____)

Multiply the constants. Add the exponents. _____

Write the results in scientific notation. _____

The radius of the Sun is _____.

Addition and Subtraction with Scientific Notation

Add 4.67×10^9 and 3.12×10^8.

Rewrite 4.67×10^9 so that 10 has an exponent of 8.

_____

Write the new addition problem _____

Add the constants. Keep the powers unchanged. _____

The constant is greater than 10, so write the result in scientific notation.

The sum is _____.

Holt McDougal Mathematics

SECTION 3A

Exponents and Roots

SECTION A: Quiz for Lessons 1 Through 4

1 Integer Exponents
Simplify.

1. 10^{-7} _____

2. $(-4)^{-3}$ _____

3. $(-3)^{-4}$ _____

4. 8^{-1} _____

5. $6 + 10^{-2}(-3)$ _____

6. $4^{-1} + 6(4)^{-2}$ _____

7. $-5^{-2} + 9^0$ _____

8. $8^{-2} - (2^0 - 2^{-3})$ _____

2 Properties of Exponents
Simplify each expression. Write your answer as a power.

9. $7^6 \cdot 7^5$

_____

10. $\dfrac{12^3}{12^3}$

_____

11. $\dfrac{t^8}{t^4}$

_____

12. $6^5 \cdot 6^{-2}$

_____

Simplify.

13. $(9^4)^{-3}$

_____

14. $(5^6)^0$

_____

15. $(-w^6)^2$

_____

16. $(7^{-3})^5$

_____

17. The hard drive on a computer holds 2^{35} bytes of data, which is 2^5 gigabytes. How many bytes is one gigabyte? _____

Holt McDougal Mathematics

Ready to Go On?

Exponents and Roots

SECTION A: Quiz for Lessons 1 Through 4, continued

3 Scientific Notation
Write each number in scientific notation.

18. 0.000027

19. 115,000,000

_____

_____

20. 0.6412

21. 10,000

_____

_____

Write each number in standard notation.

22. 7.29×10^5

23. 8×10^9

_____

_____

24. 4.5×10^{-4}

25. 5.26×10^{-6}

_____

_____

4 Operating with Scientific Notation
Perform the indicated operation. Write your answer in scientific notation.

26. $(3.6 \times 10^3) \times (4.2 \times 10^8)$ _____

27. $(2.2 \times 10^5) \div (1.1 \times 10^3)$ _____

28. $(7.35 \times 10^7) - (3.5 \times 10^5)$ _____

29. $(8.12 \times 10^6) + (11.9 \times 10^4)$ _____

30. $(5.75 \times 10^{11}) \times (6.8 \times 10^{21})$ _____

31. The diameter of a rhinovirus, which causes the common
cold, is 0.00000002 meter. The diameter of a human
hair is 10,000 times as large as a rhinovirus. What is
the diameter of a human hair? Write your answer in
scientific notation.

_____

Holt McDougal Mathematics

Ready to Go On?

Exponents and Roots

Section A Enrichment: Other Number Systems

The number system used by computers is the base 2, or binary number system. This system is different from the base 10, or decimal number system, in the following ways:

- Place values are powers of 2.
- Digits are 0, 1.

1011_{binary} = 1 eight + 0 fours + 1 two + 1 one

2^3	2^2	2^1	2^0
1	0	1	1
$1 \times 2^3 + 0 \times 2^2 + 1 \times 2^1 + 1 \times 2^0$			
8 + 0 + 2 + 1			
11			

$1011_{binary} = 11_{decimal}$

To change a number in base 10 to a number in base 2, divide by powers of 2. If there is a remainder, then divide the remainder by a smaller power of 2. Continue the process until you divide by 2^0.

Change $28_{decimal}$ to base 2.

28 is between 2^4, or 16, and 2^5, or 32.

Divide by 2^4, 2^3, 2^2, 2^1, and 2^0.

$28 \div 2^4 = 28 \div 16 = \textbf{1}$ R12
$12 \div 2^3 = 12 \div 8 \ = \textbf{1}$ R4
$\ 4 \div 2^2 = \ \ 4 \div 4 \ \ = \textbf{1}$ R0
$\ 0 \div 2^1 = \ \ 0 \div 2 \ \ = \textbf{0}$ R0
$\ 0 \div 2^0 = \ \ 0 \div 1 \ \ = \textbf{0}$ R0

$28_{decimal} = 11100_{binary}$

Change each number in base 2 to base 10.

1. 11_{binary}

2. 1010_{binary}

3. 111010_{binary}

_____

_____

_____

Change each number in base 10 to base 2.

4. $13_{decimal}$

5. $222_{decimal}$

6. $1024_{decimal}$

_____

_____

_____

Holt McDougal Mathematics

Name _____ Date _____ Class _____

Exponents and Roots

LESSON 5

Skills Intervention: Squares and Square Roots

Every positive number has two **square roots**, one positive and one negative. The positive square root is called the **principal square root**. A **perfect square** is a number that has integers as its square roots.

Vocabulary
square root
principal square root
perfect square

Perfect squares   **Not perfect squares**
25; 36; 196   12; 37; 186

The opposite of squaring a number is taking the square root.
$10^2 = 100$ $\sqrt{100} = 10$ $(-10)^2 = 100$ $-\sqrt{100} = -10$

Finding the Positive and Negative Square Roots of a Number
Find the two square roots of 49.

49

$\sqrt{49} = $ _____   What positive number multiplied by itself equals 49? _____

$-\sqrt{49} = $ _____   What negative number multiplied by itself equals 49?

_____

Geometry Application
The area of a square rug is 1,024 square feet. What is the length of its side?

$A = s^2$ Use the formula for area of a square to find the side length, s.

$1,024 = s^2$ Taking the square root of a number is the _____ of squaring a number.

$\sqrt{1,024} = \sqrt{s^2}$ Find the square root of both sides.

_____ $= s$ What is the length of the square rug? What are the units?

Can the length of a side of the rug be negative? Explain.

_____

Simplify Expressions Involving Square Roots
Simplify the expression.

$3\sqrt{36} + 5$

$3($ _____ $) + 5$ What is the square root of 36?

_____ $+ 5$ Following the order of operations what should you do first?

_____

_____   Add.

Holt McDougal Mathematics

Ready to Go On?

LESSON 5

Exponents and Roots

Problem Solving Intervention: Squares and Square Roots

You can solve some problems by finding square roots.

Each side of a small square gym is 17 meters long. A square classroom has half the area of the gym. How long is each side of the classroom? Round to the nearest whole number of meters.

Understand the Problem

1. If the area of the gym were 100 square meters, what would be the area of the classroom? _____

2. If the area of the classroom were 50 square meters, about what would be the length of each side? (*Hint:* 50 is close to 49.) _____

Make a Plan

3. How can you find the area of the gym? _____

4. How can you find the area of the classroom if you know the area of the gym?

_____

5. How can you find the length of a side of the classroom if you know its area?

_____

Solve

6. What is the area of the gym? Of the classroom?

_____

7. Round the area of the classroom to the nearest perfect square.

_____

8. How long is each side of the classroom rounded to the nearest whole number? _____

Look Back

9. Starting with your answer, show that the area of the gym is twice the area of the classroom.

_____

_____

Holt McDougal Mathematics

LESSON 6

Exponents and Roots

Skills Intervention: Estimating Square Roots

If a number is not a perfect square, you still can estimate its square root by using one of two methods:

Method 1: Use two consecutive perfect square integers that the number lies between.

Method 2: Use a calculator and round the square root to a given place.

Estimating Square Roots of Numbers

Each square root is between two consecutive integers. Name the integers.

A. $\sqrt{40}$ What perfect squares are close to 40? _____ and _____

    $6^2 =$ _____   Which perfect square is less than 40? _____

    $7^2 =$ _____   Which perfect square is greater than 40? _____

$\sqrt{40}$ is between the integers _____ and _____.

B. $-\sqrt{130}$ Which perfect squares are close to 130?

                                  _____ and _____

    $(-11)^2 =$ _____   Which perfect square is less than 130? _____

    $(-12)^2 =$ _____   Which perfect square is greater than 130? _____

$-\sqrt{130}$ is between the integers _____ and _____.

Using a Calculator to Estimate the Value of a Square Root

Use a calculator to find $\sqrt{475}$. Round to the nearest tenth.

Using a calculator, $\sqrt{475} \approx 21.7$_____. . .

What is 21.794494 rounded to the nearest tenth? _____

     Holt McDougal Mathematics

LESSON 6

Exponents and Roots

Problem Solving Intervention: Estimating Square Roots

If you drop a penny, the time it takes to hit the ground depends on the height from which you drop it. If you know *h*, the height in feet, and if you ignore the effect of air, you can use a formula to find *t*, the number of seconds it takes to fall.

$$t = \sqrt{\frac{2h}{32}}$$

How many times longer will it take a penny to drop from 576 feet than from 144 feet?

Understand the Problem

1. How long would it take a penny to drop from a height of 16 feet? _____

2. What are you being asked to compare?

_____

Make a Plan

3. How can you find the two times?

_____

4. Will you subtract or divide to compare? Why?

_____

_____

Solve

5. How long will it take the penny to fall from 576 feet? From 144 feet?

_____

6. How many times longer will it take? _____

Look Back

7. If you square both sides of the formula, you get $t^2 = \frac{2d}{32}$. Use that to check your values of *t* and *h*.

_____

_____

Holt McDougal Mathematics

Ready to Go On?

LESSON
7

Exponents and Roots

Skills Intervention: The Real Numbers

Real numbers consist of the set of rational numbers and **irrational numbers.** Irrational numbers are non-terminating, non-repeating decimals.

Vocabulary
real number
irrational number
Density Property

Real Numbers

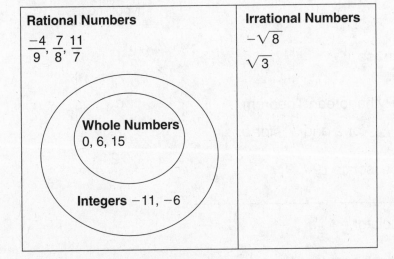

Classifying Real Numbers

Write all names that apply to each number.

A. $\sqrt{13}$

Is 13 a perfect square?

_____

Classify $\sqrt{13}$.

_____

B. −21.78

Is −21.78 a terminating or repeating

decimal? _____

Is −21.78 a rational number or irrational

number? _____

Classify −21.78. _____

The **Density Property** of real numbers states that between any two real numbers is another real number.

Applying the Density Property of Real Numbers

Find a real number between $1\frac{1}{5}$ and $1\frac{2}{5}$.

One of the many solutions is the number halfway between the two numbers.

$\left(1\frac{1}{5} + 1\frac{2}{5}\right) \div 2$ Add the numbers.

$\left(2\frac{\square}{\square}\right) \div 2 = $ _____   Divide by 2.

A number between $1\frac{1}{5}$ and $1\frac{2}{5}$ is _____.

Holt McDougal Mathematics

Ready to Go On?

Exponents and Roots

Skills Intervention: The Pythagorean Theorem

The **Pythagorean Theorem** states that in a right triangle, the sum of the squares of the lengths of the two **legs** is equal to the square of the length of the **hypotenuse.**

$a^2 + b^2 = c^2$

Vocabulary
Pythagorean Theorem
leg
hypotenuse

Finding the Length of a Hypotenuse

Find the length of the hypotenuse.

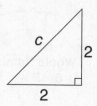

_____ $= c^2$	Write the Pythagorean Theorem.
$2^2 + 2^2 = c^2$	Substitute ___ for a and ___ for b.
$4 + 4 = c^2$	Simplify.
$\sqrt{8} = c$	How do you isolate c?
	_____
_____ $\approx c$	Use a calculator.

Finding the Length of a Leg in a Right Triangle

Solve for the unknown side in the right triangle.

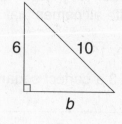

$\_^2 + b^2 = \_^2$	Substitute values for a and c.
$36 + b^2 = 100$	Simplify.
$b^2 = \_\_$	Isolate the variable.
$b = \sqrt{64}$	Take the square root of both sides.
$b = \_\_$	The length of the unknown leg is ___.

Using the Pythagorean Theorem for Measurement

Sam and Julia go to the same school. Sam lives 3 miles south of the school. Julia lives 6 miles west of the school. How far apart do Sam and Julia live from each other?

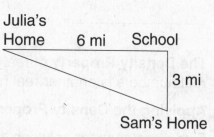

The distance Sam and Julia live from each other is the hypotenuse of a right triangle.

$a^2 + b^2 = c^2$	State the Pythagorean Theorem.
$\_^2 + \_^2 = c^2$	Substitute values for a and b.
$\_\_ + \_\_ = c^2$	Simplify.
$\_\_ = c^2$	Add.
_____ $= c$	Take the square root of both sides.
_____ $\approx c$	Use a calculator. Round to the nearest tenth.

Sam and Julia live ____ miles apart from each other.

Holt McDougal Mathematics

Ready to Go On?

LESSON
8

Exponents and Roots

Problem Solving Intervention: The Pythagorean Theorem

You can use the Pythagorean Theorem to help you find an unknown measurement.

A rectangular park is 240 feet long and 180 feet wide. What is the length of a diagonal path that connects two corners of the park?

Understand the Problem

1. Draw a diagram of the park. Label the side lengths. Show the diagonal path on your diagram.

2. What kind of triangles are formed by the diagonal and

   the sides of the park? _____

Make a Plan

3. How does the Pythagorean Theorem relate the sides lengths of a right triangle?

   _____

4. What equation states the Pythagorean Theorem? _____

5. How can you use this equation to solve the problem?

   _____

Solve

6. Substitute the values into in the Pythagorean Theorem. _____

7. Solve for c. Use your calculator. _____

8. How long is the diagonal path? _____

Look Back

9. Is your answer reasonable? Explain.

   _____

   _____

   _____

   _____

Holt McDougal Mathematics

Name _____ Date _____ Class _____

Ready to Go On?
Exponents and Roots
Skills Intervention: Applying the Pythagorean Theorem and Its Converse

You can use the Pythagorean Theorem to solve problems about lengths and distances in right triangles. The converse of the Pythagorean theorem states that if a triangle has side lengths a, b, and c, and $a^2 + b^2 = c^2$, then the triangle is a right triangle.

Fitness Application
For exercise, Keisha walks 1.8 km to Alice's house, then 0.7 km to Tino's house, and then returns back home. If the 3 streets on the map form a right triangle, what is the distance from Tino's house to Keisha's house, to the nearest hundredth?

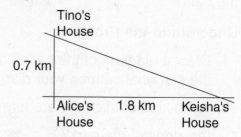

$$a^2 + b^2 = c^2$$ Use the Pythagorean Theorem.

$$\underline{\quad}^2 + \underline{\quad}^2 = c^2$$ Substitute.

$$\underline{\quad} + \underline{\quad} = c^2$$ Multiply.

$$\underline{\quad} = c^2$$ Add.

$$\sqrt{3.73} = c^2$$ Find the square root.

$$\underline{\quad} \cong c$$

The distance from Tino's to Keisha's is about _____ kilometers.

Identifying a Right Triangle
Tell whether the given side lengths form a right triangle.

A. 18, 80, 82

$$a^2 + b^2 \overset{?}{=} c^2$$ Compare $a^2 + b^2 = c^2$.

$$\underline{\quad}^2 + \underline{\quad}^2 \overset{?}{=} \underline{\quad}^2$$ Substitute.

$$\underline{\quad} + \underline{\quad} \overset{?}{=} 6{,}724$$ Simplify.

$$\underline{\quad} = 6{,}724$$ Add.

Do the side lengths for a right triangle? _____

B. 7, 25, 26

$$a^2 + b^2 \overset{?}{=} c^2$$ Compare $a^2 + b^2 = c^2$.

$$\underline{\quad}^2 + \underline{\quad}^2 \overset{?}{=} \underline{\quad}^2$$ Substitute.

$$\underline{\quad} + \underline{\quad} \overset{?}{=} 676$$ Simplify.

$$\underline{\quad} \neq 676$$ Add.

Do the side lengths for a right triangle? _____

Holt McDougal Mathematics

Ready to Go On?

Exponents and Roots

SECTION B: Quiz for Lessons 5 Through 9

5 Squares and Square Roots

Find the two square roots of each number.

1. 64   **2.** 6,084   **3.** 1,000,000   **4.** 324

_____   _____   _____   _____

5. Amy wants to put together a jigsaw puzzle that will be
24 in. × 20 in. when finished. Will the puzzle fit on a square
board with an area of 529 square inches? Explain your answer.

_____

_____

6. How many 6 in. × 6 in. square tiles will fit around
the edges of a square hallway that has an area of
1,296 square inches?   _____

6 Estimating Square Roots

Each square root is between two integers. Name the integers.
Explain your answer.

7. $-\sqrt{56}$ **8.** $\sqrt{300}$

_____   _____

_____   _____

9. $-\sqrt{250}$ **10.** $\sqrt{860}$

_____   _____

_____   _____

11. A square quilt has an area of 28 square feet. To the
nearest hundredth, what length of edging is needed
to go around all the edges of the quilt?   _____

12. The area of a square painting is 120 square inches.
Find the length of one side of the painting to the
nearest hundredth.   _____

SECTION	# Exponents and Roots
3B	**SECTION B: Quiz for Lessons 5 Through 9, continued**

7 The Real Numbers
Write all the names that apply to each number.

13. 0.26

14. $\sqrt{35}$

_____

_____

15. $\sqrt{400}$

16. $\dfrac{-\sqrt{100}}{5}$

_____

_____

17. Find a real number between $\sqrt{49}$ and 8.   _____

8 The Pythagorean Theorem
Find the missing length for each right triangle. Round your answer to the nearest tenth.

18. $a = 6$, $b = 10$, $c = ?$

19. $a = 4$, $b = ?$, $c = 12$

_____

_____

20. $a = ?$, $b = 15$, $c = 17$

21. $a = 36$, $b = 48$, $c = ?$

_____

_____

22. Jason is putting a fence around a garden. The measures of two sides that meet at a corner are 25 feet and 38 feet. For the corner to be a right angle, what would the length of the diagonal have to be?   _____

9 Applying the Pythagorean Theorem and Its Converse
Tell whether the given side lengths form a right triangle.

23. 8, 15, 17

24. 3, 6, 7

_____

_____

25. 13, 24, 25

26. 11, 60, 61

_____

_____

27. Nila folds a 8.5 in × 11 in sheet of paper along the diagonal. To the nearest tenth, what is the length of the diagonal?   _____

Holt McDougal Mathematics

Ready to Go On?

SECTION
3B
Exponents and Roots

Section B Enrichment: Proving the Pythagorean Theorem

It has been said that the Pythagorean Theorem has been proven to be true in more ways than any other theorem in mathematics. Use the diagram and complete the steps to complete one of these proofs.

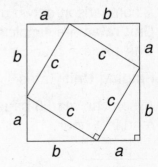

Find the area of the large square in one way.

1. Use the variables a and b to represent the length of one side of the large square.

   _____

2. Use Step 1 to write the area of the large square.   _____

3. Apply the Distributive Property to the expression in Step 2. Use exponents.

   $(a + b)(a + b) = a^2 +$ _____ + _____ + _____

4. Simplify the expression in Step 3. Remember that ab and ba represent the same quantity.   _____

Find the area of the large square in another way.

5. The area of the large square equals the area of _____

   _____ plus the area of _____.

6. Use the variable c to represent the area of the small square.   _____

7. Use the formula for the area of a triangle and the variables a and b to write the area of one triangle.   _____

8. Use Steps 6 and 7 to write the area of the large square.   _____

9. Simplify the expression in Step 8.   _____

10. Use Steps 4 and 9. Write an equation to show that the two expressions for the area of the large square are equal.   _____

11. Subtract the quantity that is the same from both sides of the equation in Step 10.   _____

12. How does the equation in Step 11 compare to the Pythagorean Theorem?

_____

Holt McDougal Mathematics

Name _____ Date _____ Class _____

Ratios, Proportions, and Similarity

LESSON 1
Skills Intervention: Ratios, Rates, and Unit Rates

A comparison of two quantities that have different units is a **rate**.
Unit rates are simplified rates in which the second quantity is one.
Unit price is a unit rate that compares the cost of item units.

Vocabulary
rate
unit rate
unit price

Finding Unit Rates

Alison can read 6 pages in 15 minutes. How many pages can she read in 1 hour?

$\dfrac{\_\_\text{pages}}{\_\_\text{minutes}}$ Write the information as a rate.

$\dfrac{\_\_\text{pages} \times \_\_}{\_\_\text{minutes} \times \_\_} = \dfrac{\_\_\text{pages}}{\_\_\text{minutes}}$ How many minutes do you want in the proportional rate? _____

$= \dfrac{\_\_\text{pages}}{\_\text{hour}}$ Alison can read _____ pages in 1 hour.

Science Application

Gold weighing 193 kg has a volume of 0.01 m³. What is the density of gold?

$\dfrac{\_\_\_\text{kg}}{\_\_\_\text{m}^3}$ Write the rate.

$\dfrac{\_\_\_\text{kg} \times \_\_\_}{\_\_\_\text{m}^3 \times \_\_\_} = \dfrac{\_\_\_\text{kg}}{1\ \text{m}^3}$ Multiply to find kilograms per 1 m³.

Gold has a density of _____ kg/m³.

Travel Application

Jessie drives 203 miles in 3.5 hours. What is his average rate of speed?

$\dfrac{\_\_\_\text{miles}}{\_\_\_\text{hours}}$ Write the rate.

$\dfrac{\_\_\_\text{miles} \div \_\_\_}{\_\_\_\text{hours} \div \_\_\_} = \dfrac{\_\_\_\text{miles}}{1\ \text{hour}}$ Divide to find miles per 1 hour.

Jessie's rate of speed is _____ per _____.

Finding Unit Prices to Compare Costs

A 14-oz box of cereal cost $3.29 and a 20-oz box of the same cereal cost $4.19. Which is the better buy?

To find the unit rate, divide the _____ by the _____.

$\dfrac{\text{price of box \#1}}{\text{number of ounces}} = \dfrac{}{_____} = _____$ $\dfrac{\text{price of box \#2}}{\text{number of ounces}} = \dfrac{}{_____} = _____$

In which box are you paying less per ounce? _____

Is the smaller or the larger box a better buy? _____

© Houghton Mifflin Harcourt Publishing Company

Ready to Go On?

LESSON 1	**Ratios, Proportions, and Similarity**

Problem Solving Intervention: Ratios, Rates, and Unit Rates

For $7.29 you can buy a pack of 8 AA batteries that comes with an additional free battery. Or you can buy a pack of 4 AA batteries for $2.89. Which costs less per battery? Explain.

Understand the Problem

1. How many batteries do you get in the package that costs $7.29? _____

Make a Plan

2. What two ratios can you compare to solve the problem?

_____

3. Suppose you knew the cost of 36 batteries when purchased in the 8-packs. Suppose you also knew the cost of 36 batteries when purchased in the 4-packs. How would that help you? Why is 36 a convenient number to use for this comparison?

_____

_____

_____

Solve

4. How many of the $7.29 packs would you need in order to get 36 batteries? What would you multiply to find how much that would cost?

_____

5. How many of the $2.89 packs would you need in order to get 36 batteries? What would you multiply to find how much that would cost?

_____

6. Estimate. Is 4 • $7.29 greater than or less than $28? Is 9 • $2.89 greater than or less than $28? Explain.

_____

_____

Look Back

7. Make sure you answer the question and explain your answer.

_____

_____

Ready to Go On?

LESSON 2 **Ratios, Proportions, and Similarity**
Skills Intervention: Solving Proportions

Cross products in proportions are equal. If the cross products are not equal then the ratios are not in proportion.

Vocabulary
cross products

Using Cross Products to Identify Proportions
Tell whether the ratios are proportional.

A. $\frac{10}{32} = \frac{8}{28}$

$\frac{10}{32} \diagdown \frac{8}{28}$ Find cross products.

$10 \times 28 =$ ____

$32 \times 8 \; =$ ____

Are the cross products equal? ____

Are the ratios proportional? ____

B. $\frac{15}{25} = \frac{6}{10}$

$\frac{15}{25} \diagdown \frac{6}{10}$ Find cross products.

$15 \times 10 =$ ____

$25 \times 6 \; =$ ____

Are the cross products equal? ____

Are the ratios proportional? ____

C. A bottle of liquid lawn fertilizer instructs you to mix one part fertilizer and 16 parts water. Is a mixture of 68 oz of water and 4 oz of fertilizer proportional to this ratio?

What is the fertilizer to water ratio given on the bottle?

____

What is the fertilizer to water ratio of the mixture?

____

$\frac{1}{16} = \frac{4}{68}$ What are the cross products? _____

Are they equal? ____

Is this a correct mixture of fertilizer? ____

Using Cross Products to Solve Proportions
Carla has driven her car 13.6 miles in 12 minutes. At this rate, how far can Carla drive in 3 hours?

$\frac{13.6}{12} = \frac{d}{180}$ Set up a proportion. Use d for the unknown distance.

$13.6 \cdot$ _____ $=$ _____ $\cdot d$ Find the cross products.

_____ $= 12d$ Multiply.

$\frac{2,448}{\boxed{}} = \frac{12d}{\boxed{}}$ Divide both sides by _____.

_____ $= d$

Carla can drive _____ miles in 3 hours.

© Houghton Mifflin Harcourt Publishing Company

Ready to Go On?

LESSON 2

Ratios, Proportions, and Similarity

Problem Solving Intervention: Solving Proportions

You can write and solve proportions to see what will happen if a rate continues.

At 2:10 P.M., your family began a 58-mile car trip to Grandma's. At 2:50 P.M., you have gone 23 miles. At this rate, will you get there by 3:30 P.M.?

Understand the Problem

1. How many miles is the whole trip to Grandma's? How many miles have you driven so far?

_____

2. Do you have to find the exact time of arrival?

_____

3. If you arrive at 3:30, how long will the whole trip have taken?

_____

Make a Plan

4. Let x be the number of minutes it takes for the whole trip. What must x be less than or equal to for you to arrive in time? _____

5. Complete the proportion to show how you could find x.

$$\frac{miles}{minutes} = \frac{miles}{x\ minutes}$$

6. Why can you estimate or use mental math to solve the problem?

_____

Solve

7. Is 58 miles greater than or less than 2 times 23 miles?

_____

8. Why must x be more than 80?

_____

Look Back

9. Make sure you answer the question that the problem asks.

_____

Holt McDougal Mathematics

SECTION 4A Ratios, Proportions, and Similarity

SECTION A: Quiz for Lessons 1 Through 2

1 Ratios, Rates, and Unit Rates

1. The mass of a chunk of titanium is 55 g. The volume is 12.5 cm^3. What is the density of the chunk of titanium? _____

2. Bixbyite is a rare mineral with a density of 4.95 g/cm^3. What is the volume of a piece of bixbyite with a mass of 101.97 g? _____

3. Maria's St. Bernard, Arfy, is fed the same amount of food every day. If Arfy gets fed 36.75 cups of dog food per week, how many cups of dog food does he get fed per day? _____

Determine the better buy.

4. 40 lb of potatoes for $11.20 or 60 lb of potatoes for $16.20 _____

5. $35.70 for 15 gallons of gas or $64.80 for 27 gallons of gas _____

2 Solving Proportions
Solve each proportion.

6. $\dfrac{12{,}000 \text{ tons}}{8 \text{ weeks}} = \dfrac{t \text{ tons}}{22 \text{ weeks}}$ _____

7. $\dfrac{440 \text{ meters}}{32 \text{ seconds}} = \dfrac{200 \text{ meters}}{s \text{ seconds}}$ _____

8. $\dfrac{464 \text{ feet}}{8 \text{ days}} = \dfrac{522 \text{ feet}}{d \text{ days}}$ _____

9. $\dfrac{\$178.50}{17 \text{ hours}} = \dfrac{\$ d}{28 \text{ hours}}$ _____

10. Jonathan conducted 24 telephone surveys in 6 hours. At this rate, how long will it take him to conduct 15 more telephone surveys? _____

Holt McDougal Mathematics

Ready to Go On?

SECTION 4A # Ratios, Proportions, and Similarity

Section A Enrichment: Acceleration

Velocity is a ratio of distance to time. Acceleration is a ratio of change in velocity to time. If a car accelerates from 50 miles/hour to 60 miles/hour in 5 seconds, the acceleration is 2 miles per hour per second.

These three equations can be used to solve problems involving acceleration:

(a) $d = v_o t + \frac{1}{2}at^2$

(b) $v_f = v_o + at$

(c) $v_f^2 - v_o^2 = 2ad$

d	Distance
v_o	Original velocity, the velocity at the beginning of acceleration
v_f	Final velocity, the velocity at the end of acceleration
a	Acceleration that is constant
t	Time, the time during which acceleration occurs

Suppose a car is traveling at 35 miles per hour and accelerates for 15 seconds at a rate of 1 mile per hour per second. How many feet does the car travel in that 15 seconds?

$d = v_o t + \frac{1}{2}at^2$

$= \left(35 \cdot \frac{5,280}{3,600}\right)(15) + \frac{1}{2}\left(\frac{5,280}{3,600}\right)(15)^2$

$= 770 + 165 = 935$ ft

$v_o = 35$ miles/hour $= 35 \cdot \frac{5,280}{3,600}$ feet/sec

$a = 1$ mile/hour/sec $= 1 \cdot \frac{5,280}{3,600}$ feet/sec$^2 = \frac{5,280}{3,600}$ feet/sec^2

$t = 15$ seconds

The car travels 935 feet.

1. A car is traveling at 45 miles per hour and accelerates for 10 seconds at a rate of 2 miles per hour per second. About how many feet does the car travel in that 10 seconds? _____

2. A motorcycle accelerates from 0 to 40 miles/hour in 8 seconds.

    a) What it its approximate rate of acceleration in feet per seconds? *Hint:* Use equation (b). _____

    b) How many feet does it travel in that period of time? _____

3. A truck accelerates from 0 to 60 miles/hour with a constant acceleration of 1.5 miles/hour/sec. How many feet does it travel in the time it takes to reach 60 miles/hour. *Hint:* Use equation (c). _____

4. Form three different formulas for acceleration, each one based on one of the equations given above. _____

Holt McDougal Mathematics

Ready to Go On?

LESSON 3

Ratios, Proportions, and Similarity

Skills Intervention: Similar Figures

Congruent figures have the same size and the same shape, whereas **similar** figures have the same shape but not always the same size. In similar polygons **corresponding angles** must be congruent and **corresponding sides** must have lengths that form equivalent ratios.

Vocabulary
similar
corresponding sides
corresponding angles

Finding Missing Measures in Similar Figures

A standard 4 inch long by 6 inch wide photo is scaled down to 1.5 inch long to fit in a photo key chain. How wide should the picture be in the key chain for the two pictures to be similar?

What is the known length of the scaled picture? _____

What is the corresponding length of the original picture? _____

_____   Divide the known length by the corresponding length.

This is the _____.

6 in. × _____ = _____   Multiply the width of the original picture by the scale factor.

What is the width of the new picture? _____

Architecture Application

An architect draws a blueprint of a house. He draws the length of the house 15 inches and the width 6 inches. If the actual length is 60 feet, what is the width?

What is the length of the house on the blueprint? _____

What is the width of the house on the blueprint? _____

What is the length of the actual house? _____

What is the unknown? _____

Set up a proportion as shown.

$$\frac{\text{blueprint length}}{\text{blueprint width}} = \frac{\text{actual length}}{\text{actual width}}$$ _____

What are the cross products? _____ • x ft = _____ • 6 in.

Are the same units on both sides of the equal sign? _____ Cancel them.

Multiply each side.   _____ = _____

Divide to isolate x. x = _____

What is the width of the actual house? _____

Holt McDougal Mathematics

Ready to Go On?

LESSON 3
Ratios, Proportions, and Similarity

Problem Solving Intervention: Similar Figures

Similar figures have the same shape, but not necessarily the same size. The ratio formed by corresponding sides is the scale factor.

A photo of a candidate for mayor is 6 inches tall and 4.5 inches wide. It is being enlarged to become a campaign poster that will be 2.5 feet tall. How wide will the poster be, if the pictures are similar?

Understand the Problem

1. What is true about the sides and angles of similar figures?

_____

2. Identify the corresponding sides of the photo and poster.

_____

_____

_____

Make a Plan

3. Using the ratio of the scale factor on one side of an equation, what can you form with another ratio to help you find the unknown width of the poster?

_____

4. In order to compare equivalent units, what dimension should you use in the equation for the height of the poster? _____

Solve

5. Form a proportion using *x* for the unknown width of the poster.

_____

6. Cross multiply then simplify to isolate *x*. What will be the width of the poster? _____

Look Back

7. The photo and poster are similar figures, so the ratio of height to width for each should be the same. Show whether this is true.

_____

LESSON 4

Ratios, Proportions, and Similarity

Skills Intervention: Dilations

A **dilation** is an enlargement or reduction of a figure without changing its shape. A **scale factor** describes how much a figure is enlarged or reduced. The **center of dilation** is a fixed point that connects each pair of corresponding vertices.

Vocabulary
dilation
center of dilation
scale factor

Identifying Dilations

Tell whether each transformation is a dilation.

A.

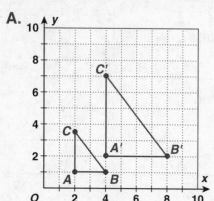

B.

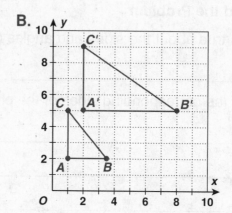

Is the transformation a dilation? ____

Is the transformation a dilation? ____

Using the Origin as the Center of Dilation

Dilate the figure by a scale factor of $\frac{3}{4}$. What are the coordinates of the image?

What do you need to multiply each coordinate by? _____

$\triangle ABC$ $\qquad\qquad$ $\triangle A'B'C'$

$A(2, 6) \rightarrow A'\left(2 \cdot \dfrac{3}{4}, 6 \cdot \dfrac{3}{4}\right) \rightarrow A'$ _____

$B(4, 6) \rightarrow B'\left(4 \cdot \dfrac{3}{4}, 6 \cdot \dfrac{3}{4}\right) \rightarrow B'$ _____

$C(4, 8) \rightarrow C'\left(4 \cdot \dfrac{3}{4}, 8 \cdot \dfrac{3}{4}\right) \rightarrow C'$ _____

Sketch the dilated figure on the same coordinate plane.

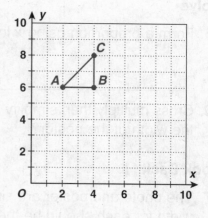

Holt McDougal Mathematics

LESSON
4

Ready to Go On?
Ratios, Proportions, and Similarity
Problem Solving Intervention: Dilations

For some problems, you can choose coordinates that will be easy to work with.

A square with an area of 16 cm^2 is dilated with a scale factor of 2.5. What is the area of the dilated square?

Understand the Problem

1. Will the area of the dilated square be greater than 16 cm^2? Explain.

   _____

2. By what number would you multiply the coordinates of a vertex on the square to find its new coordinates after the dilation? _____

Make a Plan

3. How would it help to draw the original square on a coordinate plane?

   _____

   _____

4. Why would it make sense to use (0,0) as one corner?

   _____

5. What is the length of the original square? Explain.

   _____

   _____

Solve

6. On the grid, draw the original square with the lower left corner at (0, 0). Label the coordinates of each corner of the square.

7. Multiply to find the coordinates of the corners of the dilated square. Draw it and label the coordinates of each corner.

8. What is the area of the dilated square?

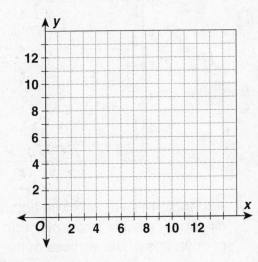

   _____

Look Back

9. Make sure your multiplication and your diagram are accurate.

Holt McDougal Mathematics

Ready to Go On?

Ratios, Proportions, and Similarity

SECTION B: Quiz for Lessons 3 Through 4

3 Similar Figures

1. Which rectangles are similar? _____

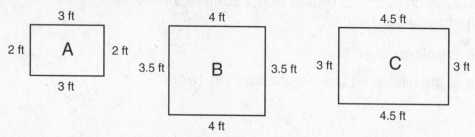

2. Jaime found a picture that he wanted to fit into a collage he was making. The picture was 5 inches wide and 4 inches tall. He enlarged the picture to a width of 12.5 inches. How tall was the enlarged picture?   _____

3. Laura had a photo of her dog that she wanted to enlarge to fill a frame. The original photo was 5 inches wide and 8 inches tall. The enlargement was 9.6 inches tall. How wide was the enlargement? _____

4. A computer screen contained the picture of an office building. The measurement of the building on the screen was 14 cm tall by 2.6 cm wide. The image was projected onto a wall where the height of the building measured 91 cm. What was the width of the building as measured on the wall?   _____

4 Dilations

Tell whether the transformation is a dilation.

5. _____
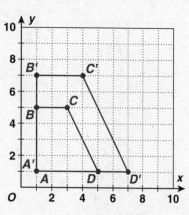

6. _____
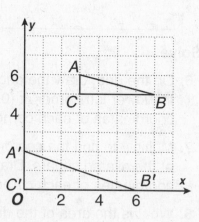

7. A triangle has vertices with coordinates (0,0), (−3, 4), and (5, −1). If the triangle is dilated by a scale factor of 2 with the origin as the center of dilation, what are the coordinates of the vertices of the image?

_____

Holt McDougal Mathematics

SECTION 4B Ready to Go On?
Ratios, Proportions, and Similarity
Section B Enrichment: Aspect Ratios

Aspect ratio is the ratio of the width of a picture to the height of a
picture. The screens of traditional television sets have an aspect
ratio of 4:3, or 1.33:1. One common aspect ratio used for films today
is the widescreen format of 1.85:1.

1. The diagram on the right shows what
   happens when the full height of a movie
   with an aspect ratio of 1.85:1 is shown on a
   standard TV screen. About what percent of
   the original image appears to get cut off?

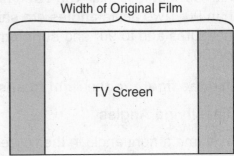

Width of Original Film

TV Screen

_____

The situation gets a little more interesting when the full width
of a movie with an aspect ratio of 1.85:1 is shown centered on
a standard TV screen.

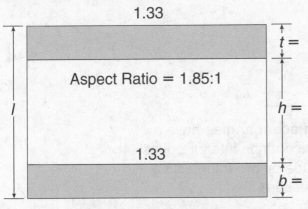

1.33

Aspect Ratio = 1.85:1

1.33

l

t =

h =

b =

2. In the diagram, the width of the 1.85:1 film is shown
   conforming to the width of the 1.33:1 TV screen. Write
   and solve a proportion to find the relative height *h* of
   the displayed film. Fill in that dimension on the
   diagram, leaving it as a fraction.   _____

3. The unused areas of the TV screen, shown in gray, are equal
   in size. Use the dimension you found for *h* to determine relative
   dimensions for *t* and *b*. Fill in those dimensions on the diagram
   leaving them as fractions.

4. About what percent of the TV screen is used by the film image?
   How does that compare with your answer to question 1?

_____

_____

_____

Name _____ Date _____ Class _____

An **angle** is made of two rays with a common vertex.

A **right angle** measures 90°, an **obtuse angle** measures greater than 90° but less than 180°, and an **acute angle** measures less than 90°. Two acute **angles** are said to be **complementary** if their measures add to 90° and **supplementary** if their measures add to 180°.

<table>
<tr><td>Vocabulary</td></tr>
<tr><td>right angle</td></tr>
<tr><td>obtuse angle</td></tr>
<tr><td>acute angle</td></tr>
<tr><td>angle</td></tr>
<tr><td>complementary
  angles</td></tr>
<tr><td>supplementary
  angles</td></tr>
<tr><td>adjacent angles</td></tr>
<tr><td>vertical angles</td></tr>
<tr><td>congruent angles</td></tr>
</table>

Use the figure to the right to answer each question.

Classifying Angles

A. Name a right angle in the figure.

How many degrees are in a right angle?

_____

Name a right angle. _____

B. Name two obtuse angles in the figure.

An obtuse angle has a measure greater

than _____ but less than _____.

Name two obtuse angles. _____

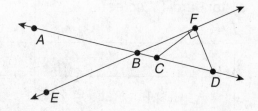

Some angles have special relationships. **Adjacent angles** have a common vertex and a common side, but no common interior points. **Vertical angles** are nonadjacent angles made by two intersecting lines. **Congruent angles** have the same measure.

Finding Angle Measures
Use the diagram to find the angle measure.

If m∠*CBF* = 40°, find m∠*FBA*.

m∠*CBF* + m∠*FBA* = _____   The angles are _____.

_____ + m∠*FBA* = _____   Substitute _____ for m∠*CBF*.

<u>−40°</u>   <u>−40°</u>   Subtract _____ from both sides.

    m∠*FBA* = _____

Ready to Go On?

LESSON 2 Geometric Relationships

Skills Intervention: Parallel and Perpendicular Lines

Parallel lines are two lines in a plane that never meet and **perpendicular lines** intersect at 90° angles. A line that intersects two or more lines is called a **transversal.** When two parallel lines are intersected by a transversal, the acute angles and obtuse angles that are formed are congruent and any acute angle is supplementary to any obtuse angle.

Vocabulary
parallel lines
perpendicular lines
transversal

Identifying Congruent Angles Formed by a Transversal

Lines *m* and *n* are parallel. Use a protractor to measure the angles formed when the transversal intersects the parallel lines. Which angles seem to be congruent?

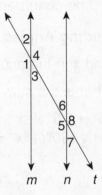

Find the measure of:

∠1 _____   ∠2 _____   ∠3 _____   ∠4 _____

∠5 _____   ∠6 _____   ∠7 _____   ∠8 _____

Which angles are congruent to ∠2? _____ _____ and _____

Which angles are congruent to ∠1? _____ _____ and _____

Finding Angle Measures of Parallel Lines Cut by Transversals

In the figure, line *p* ‖ line *q*. Find the measure of each angle.

A. ∠7

What type of angle is ∠7? _____

What is the measure of the angle opposite ∠7? _____

When parallel lines are cut by a transversal, all obtuse

angles are _____.

So, m∠7 = _____.

B. ∠5

When parallel lines are cut by a transversal, any _____ angle

formed is supplementary to any _____ angle formed.

What is the sum of two supplementary angles? _____

∠5 is _____ to 118°.

m∠5 + 118° = _____   Write an equation to find m∠5.

 −118°   −118°   Subtract.

m∠5   = _____

Holt McDougal Mathematics

LESSON 3 **Geometric Relationships**

Skills Intervention: Triangles

Vocabulary
Triangle Sum
  Theorem
acute triangle
right triangle
obtuse triangle
equilateral triangle
isosceles triangle
scalene triangle
Triangle Inequality
  Theorem

The **Triangle Sum Theorem** states that the angle measures of
any triangle in a plane add up to 180°. Triangles are classified
by their angle measures. **Acute triangles** have 3 acute angles.
Right triangles have 1 right angle. **Obtuse triangles** have
1 obtuse angle. Triangles are also classified by their side lengths.
Equilateral triangles have 3 congruent sides and 3 congruent
angles. **Isosceles triangles** have at least 2 congruent sides and
2 congruent angles. **Scalene triangles** have no congruent sides
and no congruent angles.

Finding Angles in Acute and Right Triangles

Find x in the acute triangle.

What is the sum of the angles in an acute triangle? _____

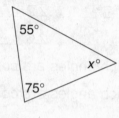

$55° + 75° + x° =$ _____

$\quad\quad 130° + x° = 180°$ Add.

_____   _____   What should you subtract from
                           each side to isolate x?

$\quad\quad x° =$ _____   What is the measure of x?

The **Triangle Inequality Theorem** states that the sum of the lengths
of any two sides of a triangle is greater than the length of the third
side.

Using the Triangle Inequality Theorem

Tell whether a triangle can have sides with the given lengths.
3 ft, 6 ft, 8 ft

Find the sum of the lengths of two sides, and compare it to the
third side.

$3 +$ _____ $\overset{?}{>} 8$ _____ $+ 8 \overset{?}{>} 6$ $8 + 6 \overset{?}{>}$ _____

_____ > 8 _____ > 6 _____ > 3

Is the sum of the lengths of any two sides
greater than the length of the third side?   _____

Can a triangle have these side lengths?   _____

Holt McDougal Mathematics

Name _____ Date _____ Class _____

LESSON 4

Geometric Relationships

Skills Intervention: Coordinate Geometry

The **midpoint** of a line segment is the point that divides the
segment into two congruent segments.

Vocabulary
midpoint

Finding the Coordinates of a Missing Vertex

Find the coordinates of the missing vertex.

Triangle *DEF* has a right angle at *E* and $\overline{EF}$ = 3. Find possible
coordinates for *F*.

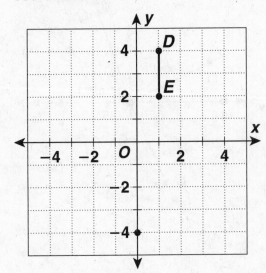

Since $\overline{DE}$ is vertical, $\overline{EF}$ must be _____
to make a right angle.

Point *F* could be _____ units to the left of point
E, at (_____, _____).

Point *F* could also be _____ units to the right of
point *E*, at (_____, _____)

The possible coordinates for *F* are (_____, _____) and (_____, _____).

Finding the Coordinates of a Midpoint

Find the coordinates of the midpoint of $\overline{AB}$.

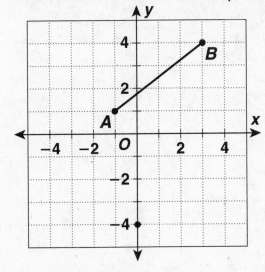

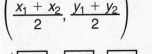

$$\left(\frac{x_1 + x_2}{2}, \frac{y_1 + y_2}{2} \right)$$

Use the midpoint formula.

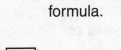

$$\left(\frac{\Box + \Box}{2}, \frac{\Box + \Box}{2} \right)$$ The endpoints are

A(____, ____)
and *B*(____, ____).

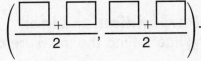

$$\left(\Box, \Box \right)$$

Simplify.

The coordinates for the midpoint of segment *AB* are _____.

63 **Holt McDougal Mathematics**

Ready to Go On?

SECTION 5A

Geometric Relationships

SECTION A: Quiz for Lessons 1 Through 4

1 Angle Relationships

Refer to the figure.

1. Name two pairs of complementary angles.

_____

2. Name three pairs of supplementary angles above line $\overleftrightarrow{AE}$.

_____

_____

3. Name one right angle. _____

4. How many rays are in the figure? _____

5. Name the segments identified on line $\overleftrightarrow{AE}$.

_____

6. How many points, in addition to those identified, are located on plane ABC?

_____

Refer to the figure.

7. Name the right angle. _____

8. Name two acute angles. _____

9. Name two obtuse angles. _____

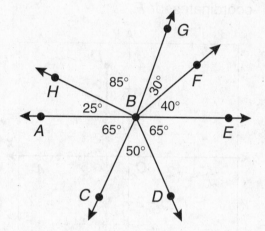

2 Parallel and Perpendicular Lines

In the figure, line t || line r. Find the measure of each angle.

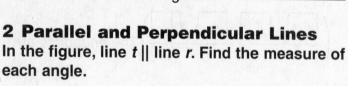

10. ∠1 _____   11. ∠2 _____

12. ∠3 _____   13. ∠4 _____

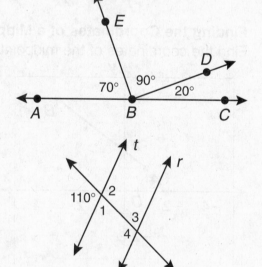

© Houghton Mifflin Harcourt Publishing Company

Holt McDougal Mathematics

Ready to Go On?

Geometric Relationships

SECTION A: Quiz for Lessons 1 Through 4, continued

3 Triangles

Find *x*° in each triangle.

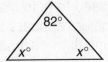
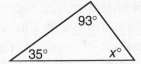

14. _____   15. _____

Find *x*° in each triangle.

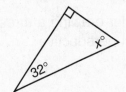

16. _____   17. _____

4 Coordinate Geometry

Graph the quadrilaterals with the given vertices. Give all of the names that apply to each quadrilateral.

18. *A*(4, 4), *B*(4, −2), *C*(−3, −2), *D*(−2, 4)

19. *P*(2, 4), *Q*(2, −1), *R*(−1, −1), *S*(−1, 4)

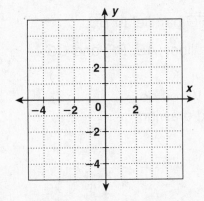

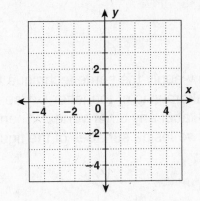

Name the coordinates of the missing vertex.

20. rectangle *ABCD* with *A*(−3, 2), *B*(4, 2), *C*(4, −3)

_____

21. parallelogram *PQRS* with *P*(−3, 2), *Q*(−1, 4), *R*(2, −1)

_____

Holt McDougal Mathematics

Ready to Go On?

SECTION 5A **Geometric Relationships**

Section A Enrichment: Single Point Perspective

Perspective is a technique used to help make a drawing of an object appear the way the actual object appears to the human eye. A main feature of perspective drawing is that some edges that are parallel in an actual object are not drawn as parallel line segments. These non-parallel lines converge at a "vanishing point."

These are the steps for drawing a three-dimensional rectangular solid with single point perspective.

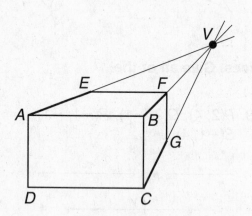

Steps

1. Draw rectangle *ABCD*.

2. Choose any vanishing point *V* you wish.

3. Draw light lines from each vertex of rectangle *ABCD* through point *V*.

4. Choose a point *E* on line *AV*. Draw a line from *E* that is parallel to $\overline{AB}$ and intersects $\overline{BV}$ at *F*.

5. Draw $\overline{FG}$ parallel to $\overline{BC}$.

6. Darken lines *AE*, *BF*, and *CG*.

You can now apply the same technique to create a three-dimensional drawing of the letter L. Use vanishing point *V*. You do not have to label any other vertex. When you are finished drawing, shade the two inside surfaces of the figure.

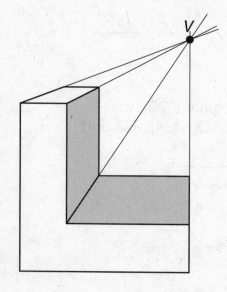

Ready to Go On?

LESSON 5

Geometric Relationships

Skills Intervention: Congruence

Two figures are **congruent figures** if all corresponding sides and angles are congruent. When writing congruence statements between a pair of polygons, the vertices in the second figure are written in order of **correspondence** with the first figure.

Writing Congruence Statements

Write a congruence statement for the pair of polygons.

 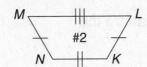

In polygon #2, which angle is congruent and in the same position as

∠W in polygon #1? _____

In polygon #2, which angle is congruent and in the same position as

∠X in polygon #1? _____

Complete the following statements.

∠Y ≅ ∠K so _____ corresponds to ∠K.

∠Z ≅ _____ so ∠Z corresponds to _____.

Complete the statement: trapezoid WZYX ≅ trapezoid _____.

Using Congruence Relationships to Find Unknown Values

pentagon HIJKL ≅ pentagon TPQRS

A. Find m.

What angle corresponds to ∠K? _____

What is the measure of these angles? _____

5m = 100   Write an equation to find m.

$\dfrac{5m}{\underline{\quad}} = \dfrac{100}{\underline{\quad}}$ Divide to isolate m.

m = _____   Solve for m.

B. Find n.

What side does n + 10 correspond to? _____

n + 10 = 20   Write an equation.

$\underline{}\quad\underline{}$ Undo the addition.

n = ___   Solve for n.

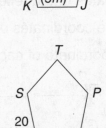

      Holt McDougal Mathematics

Ready to Go On?

LESSON 6

Geometric Relationships

Skills Intervention: Transformations

Three types of **transformations** are:
Translation: slides a figure along a line without turning.
Rotation: turns the figure around a point, called the **center of rotation.**
Reflection: flips the figure across a line to create a mirror **image.**

Graphing Transformations on a Coordinate Plane

If triangle *ABC* is translated 4 units right, what are the

coordinates of the image of point *A*? _____

Translate triangle *ABC* 4 units right and label the image
$A_1B_1C_1$.

If triangle *ABC* is rotated 180° clockwise about (0, 0), the

rotated image of side *BC* will be _____ to side *BC*.

Rotate triangle *ABC* 180° clockwise about (0, 0) and label
the image $A_2B_2C_2$.

If triangle *ABC* is reflected across the *x*-axis, what are the

coordinates of the image of point *C*? _____

Reflect triangle *ABC* across the *x*-axis and label the image $A_3B_3C_3$.

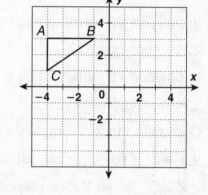

Graphing Reflections on a Coordinate Plane

Graph the reflection of quadrilateral *FGHJ* across the *y*-axis.

If quadrilateral *FGHJ* is reflected across the *y*-axis, will the
x-coordinates of the reflection stay the same?   _____

If quadrilateral *FGHJ* is reflected across the *y*-axis, will the
y-coordinates of the reflection stay the same?   _____

To find the coordinates of the reflection, multiply the

_____-coordinate of each vertex by _____.

$F(2, 4) \rightarrow F'(\underline{\hspace{0.8cm}}, \underline{\hspace{0.8cm}})$

$G(3, 2) \rightarrow G'(\underline{\hspace{0.8cm}}, \underline{\hspace{0.8cm}})$

$H(3, 1) \rightarrow H'(\underline{\hspace{0.8cm}}, \underline{\hspace{0.8cm}})$

$J(1, 2) \rightarrow J'(\underline{\hspace{0.8cm}}, \underline{\hspace{0.8cm}})$

Graph *F'G'H'J'*.

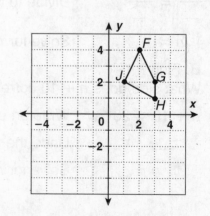

Ready to Go On?

LESSON 7 **Geometric Relationships**

Skills Intervention: Similarity and Congruence Transformations

Identifying Similarity Transformations

Identify the transformation from the original to the image and tell whether the two figures are similar or congruent?

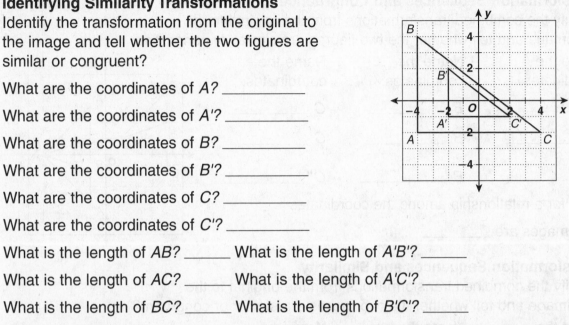

What are the coordinates of A? _____

What are the coordinates of A'? _____

What are the coordinates of B? _____

What are the coordinates of B'? _____

What are the coordinates of C? _____

What are the coordinates of C'? _____

What is the length of AB? _____ What is the length of A'B'? _____

What is the length of AC? _____ What is the length of A'C'? _____

What is the length of BC? _____ What is the length of B'C'? _____

Look for a relationship among the coordinates. Look for a relationship among the lengths of the sides.

The transformation is a _____ and the figures are _____ .

Identifying Congruence Transformations

Identify the transformation from the original to the image and tell whether the two figures are similar or congruent?

What are the coordinates of A? _____

What are the coordinates of A'? _____

What are the coordinates of B? _____

What are the coordinates of B'? _____

What are the coordinates of C? _____

What are the coordinates of C'? _____

What is the length of AB? _____ What is the length of A'B'? _____

What is the length of AC? _____ What is the length of A'C'? _____

What is the length of BC? _____ What is the length of B'C'? _____

Look for a relationship among the coordinates. Look for a relationship among the lengths of the sides.

The transformation is a _____ and the figures are _____.

Holt McDougal Mathematics

Ready to Go On?

LESSON 8

Geometric Relationships

Skills Intervention: Identifying Combined Transformations

Transformation Sequences and Congruence

Identify the combined transformations from the original to the
final image and tell whether the two figures are similar or congruent?

Name the coordinates.	Name the coordinates.	Name the coordinates.
A _____	B _____	C _____
A' _____	B' _____	C' _____
A" _____	B" _____	C" _____

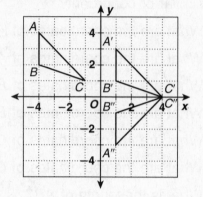

Look for a relationship among the coordinates

The images are _____.

Transformation Sequences and Similarity

Identify the combined transformations from the original to the
final image and tell whether the two figures are similar or congruent?

Name the coordinates.	Name the coordinates.	Name the coordinates.
A _____	A' _____	A" _____
B _____	B' _____	B" _____
C _____	C' _____	C" _____
D _____	D' _____	D" _____
E _____	E' _____	E" _____

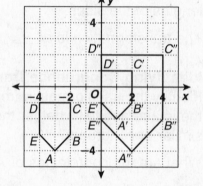

Look for a relationship among the coordinates
The original and final images are _____.

Finding Sequences of Transformations

Find a sequence of at least two combined
transformations from the original to the final image.
What are the coordinates of the vertices of *ABCD?*

_____

What are the coordinates of the vertices of *A'B'C'D'*?

_____

What are the coordinates of the vertices of *A"B"C"D"*?

_____

The sequence has _____ transformations.

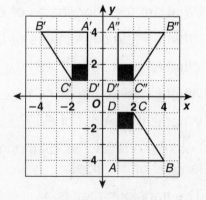

Holt McDougal Mathematics

Ready to Go On?

SECTION **5B** **Geometric Relationships**

5B SECTION B: Quiz for Lessons 5 Through 8

5 Congruence

In the figure, triangle *DEF* ≅ triangle *RST*.

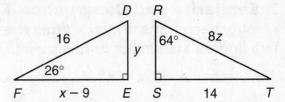

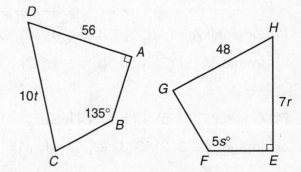

1. Find *x.* _____

2. Find *z.* _____

In the figure, quadrilateral *ABCD* ≅
quadrilateral *EFGH*

3. Find *r.* _____

4. Find *s.* _____

5. Find *t.* _____

6 Transformations

Identify each as a translation, reflection, rotation, or none of these.

6.

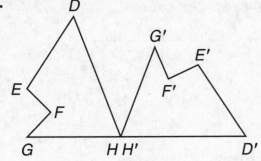

7.

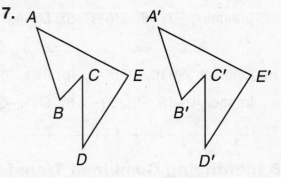

_____   _____

Quadrilateral *JKLM* has vertices *J*(0, 0), *K*(5, 0), *L*(4, −4),
M(0, −6). Find the coordinates of the image of each point after
each transformation.

8. 90° clockwise rotation about (0,0),
point *K*

9. reflection across the *y*-axis, point *J*

_____   _____

10. translation 5 units up, point *L*

11. 180° clockwise rotation about (0,0),
point *M*

_____   _____

SECTION
5B
Geometric Relationships

SECTION B: Quiz for Lessons 5 Through 8, continued

7 Similarity and Congruence Transformations

Identify each transformation from the original to the image, and tell whether the two figures are similar or congruent.

12. Original: $A(-2, 5)$, $B(3, 5)$, $C(3, -1)$, $D(-2, -1)$

Image: $A'(2, 5)$, $B'(-3, 5)$, $C'(-3, -1)$, $D'(2, -1)$

_____

13. Original: $A(-4, 8)$, $B(0, 4)$, $C(-4, -8)$, $D(-8, -4)$

Image: $A'(-1, 2)$, $B'(0, 1)$, $C'(-1, -2)$, $D'(-2, -1)$

_____

14. Original: $A(0, 5)$, $B(5, 1)$, $C(1, 2)$

Image: $A'(-2, 2)$, $B'(3, -2)$, $C'(-1, -1)$

_____

15. Original: $A(-8, 7)$, $B(-5, 3)$, $C(-2, 4)$, $D(1, 6)$

Image: $A'(-7, -8)$, $B'(-3, -5)$, $C'(-4, -2)$, $D'(-6, 1)$

_____

16. Original: $A(-10, 2)$, $B(-3, -6)$, $C(1, 3)$

Image: $A'(-10, -2)$, $B'(-3, 6)$, $C'(1, -3)$

_____

8 Identifying Combined Transformations

Identify the combined transformations from the original to the final image, and tell whether the two figures are similar or congruent.

17.

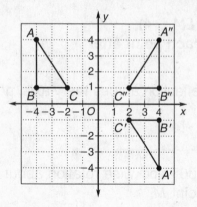

18.

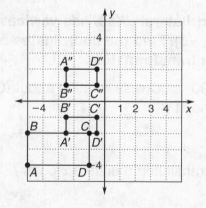

_____   _____

_____   _____

_____   _____

Holt McDougal Mathematics

Ready to Go On?

SECTION **5B**
Geometric Relationships
Section B Enrichment: Frieze Designs

A frieze is a pattern that repeats in one direction. It consists of repeated copies of a single figure or block. Frieze patterns, also called border patterns, can be found along the upper edge of wallpaper, on pottery, as decorative design on buildings, and elsewhere. An example of a frieze is below.

As you can see, the same triangle is repeated and it has been reflected horizontally. Name the translation used to make the frieze below.

Five basic transformations used for friezes are listed below at the right. Match each transformation with the frieze that incorporates it.

Rotation _____

Translation _____

Reflection Across
a Horizontal Line _____

Reflection Across
a Vertical Line _____

Glide Reflection _____

Holt McDougal Mathematics

Name _____ Date _____ Class _____

Measurement and Geometry

Skills Intervention: Circles

A **circle** is a set of points in a plane that are a fixed distance from a given point, called the center.

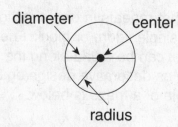

diameter   center

radius

The **circumference** is the distance around a circle, $C = \pi d$ or $C = 2\pi r$. The formula for the area of a circle is $A = \pi r^2$.

Finding the Circumference of a Circle

Find the circumference of each circle both in terms of π and to the nearest tenth of a unit. Use 3.14 for π.

A. circle with radius 6 cm

$C =$ _____   Write the formula for the circumference of a circle, if you know the radius.

$C = 2\pi\left(\underline{}\right)$ What do you substitute for r?

$C = \underline{}\pi$ cm   Multiply.

Using a calculator 12π is $\approx$ _____ cm.

What is 37.68 rounded to the nearest tenth? _____

B. circle with diameter 2.5 in.

$C =$ _____   Write the formula for the circumference of a circle, if you know the diameter.

$C = \pi\left(\underline{}\right)$ Substitute the value for d into the equation.
$C = 2.5\pi$ in.   Multiply.

$\approx$ _____ in.   Use a calculator. Round to the nearest tenth.

Finding the Area of a Circle

Find the area of the circle both in terms of π and to the nearest tenth. Use 3.14 for π.

circle with diameter 2.5 in.
$A = \pi r^2$

$r = \dfrac{d}{2} = \dfrac{\overline{}}{2} = $ _____   What is the relationship between the radius and diameter of a circle?

_____

$A = \pi\left(\underline{}^2\right)$ Substitute the value of r into the formula.

$A \approx$ _____ in^2 What is the area to the nearest tenth?

Holt McDougal Mathematics

Name _____ Date _____ Class _____

LESSON 2

Measurement and Geometry

Skills Intervention: Volume of Prisms and Cylinders

A prism is a three-dimensional figure named for the shape of its base. A cylinder is a geometric solid with two circular bases. The volume of a solid is the number of cubic units needed to fill the figure. Use these formulas to find the volume.

Prism: $V = Bh$ Cylinder: $V = Bh = (\pi r^2)h$

Finding the Volume of Prisms and Cylinders
Find the volume to the nearest tenth of a unit.

A. What shape is the base of the figure? _____

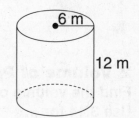

4 m
8 m
2 m

How do you find the area of a rectangle? _____

$B = 2 \cdot 4 =$ ___ m^2 Find the area of the base.

$V =$ ____   What is the formula for the volume of a prism?

$V = 8 \cdot$ ___   Substitute known values into the formula.

$V =$ ___ m^3 What is the volume?

B. What shape is the base of the figure? _____

How do you find the area of the base? _____

What is the length of the radius? _____

$B = \pi(6^2)$ Find the area of the base.

$B =$ ____ m^2

6 m
12 m

$V =$ ____   Write the formula for the volume of a cylinder.

$V =$ ____ • ____   What values do you substitute for B and h?

$V =$ _____ π Multiply.

$V \approx$ _____ m^3 Multiply.

C. What shape is the base of the figure? _____

How do you find the area of a triangle? _____

4 ft
6 ft
13 ft

$B = \frac{1}{2} \cdot$ _____ $=$ ___ ft^2 What is the area of the base?

What is the formula for the volume of a prism? _____

What values do you substitute for B and h? _____

$V = Bh$ Find the volume of the prism.

$V =$ ___ • ___

$V =$ ____ ft^3

Holt McDougal Mathematics

Ready to Go On?

Measurement and Geometry

SECTION A: Quiz for Lessons 1 Through 2

1 Circles

Find the area and circumference of each circle, both in terms of
π and to the nearest tenth. Use 3.14 for π.

1. radius = 14 cm

_____

_____

2. diameter = 8 yd

3. Graph a circle with center (1, 0) that passes through
(1, 2). Find the area and circumference, both in terms
of π (and to the nearest tenth). Use 3.14 for π.

_____

_____

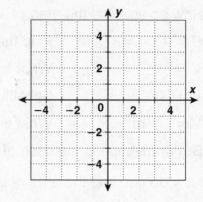

2 Volume of Prisms and Cylinders

Find the volume of each figure to the nearest tenth.
Use 3.14 for π.

4.

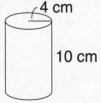

4 cm

10 cm

_____

5.

8.5 in.

7 in.

5 in.

_____

6.

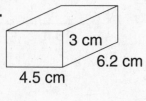

3 cm

6.2 cm

4.5 cm

_____

7.

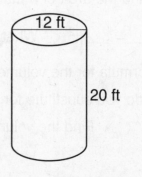

12 ft

20 ft

_____

Holt McDougal Mathematics

Ready to Go On?

SECTION 6A Measurement and Geometry

Section A Enrichment: Bicycle Rotations

When you pedal a bicycle, it makes the wheels rotate and the biker moves forward. Common sizes of bicycle wheels are 12", 24", 26", and 29". Older bicycle may have wheels that are 27". These sizes represent the diameter of the wheel.

1. What measurement of a circle is one complete rotation of a wheel?

_____

2. Complete the table for each size bicycle wheel to find the distance traveled for one complete rotation. Use 3.14 for π and round to the nearest hundredth

Length of Diameter	12"	24"	26"	27"	29"
in inches	___	___	___	___	___
in feet	___	___	___	___	___

For Questions 3–8, round to the nearest whole number.

3. If you ride a 26" bike 500 feet, how many rotations will the tires make?

_____

4. If you ride a 29" bike 1,200 feet, how many rotations will the tires make?

_____

5. If you ride a 12" bike 500 feet, how many rotations will the tires make?

_____

6. If you ride a 27" bike 1 mile, how many rotations will the tires make?

_____

7. If you ride a 24" bike 5 miles, how many rotations will the tires make?

_____

8. If you ride a 26" bike and wanted to take a trip where you would have one million rotations, how far in miles would you travel?

_____

Holt McDougal Mathematics

Name _____ Date _____ Class _____

Measurement and Geometry

Skills Intervention: Volume of Pyramids and Cones

A pyramid is named for the shape of its base. A cone has a circular base. The height of a pyramid or cone is the distance from the highest point to the base along a perpendicular line. Use these formulas to calculate volume.

Pyramid: $V = \frac{1}{3}Bh$ Cone: $V = \frac{1}{3}\pi r^2 h$

Finding the Volume of Pyramids and Cones

Find the volume.

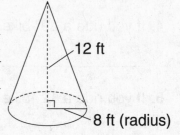

A. What type of base does the figure have? _____

How do you find the area of the base? _____

$B = 6 \cdot 6 = 36$ in^2

$V = \frac{1}{3}Bh$ In the volume formula what does the h represent?

_____

What does the B represent? _____

$V = \frac{1}{3}(\underline{\quad})$ What values do you substitute for B and h?

$V = \underline{\quad}$ in^3 What is the volume of the pyramid?

B. What type of figure is shown? _____

What shape is the base? _____

How do you find the area of the base? _____

Find the area of the base. $A = \pi\underline{\quad}^2 = \underline{\quad}\pi$ ft^2

What is the formula for the volume of a cone? _____

Substitute for B and h. $V = \frac{1}{3}\left(\underline{\quad}\pi \cdot \underline{\quad}\right)$

$V = \underline{\quad}\pi$ Use 3.14 for π.

$V = \underline{\quad\quad}$ ft^3 Multiply.

Ready to Go On?

LESSON
4

Measurement and Geometry
Skills Intervention: Spheres

A **sphere** is a set of points in three dimensions that are a fixed distance from a given point.

Volume Formula   Surface Area Formula

$V = \frac{4}{3}\pi r^3$ $S = 4\pi r^2$

Finding the Volume of a Sphere
Find the volume of a sphere with radius 2 ft, both in terms of π and to the nearest tenth of a unit.

What is the formula for the volume of a sphere? $V =$ _____

What value will you substitute for r? $V = \frac{4}{3}\pi\left(\underline{}\right)^3$

Simplify the power. $V = \frac{4}{3}\pi\underline{}$

Multiply. $V = \frac{\overline{}}{3}\pi$

Use 3.14 for π. $V \approx \underline{}$ ft^3

The volume of a sphere with a radius of 2 ft is _____.

The surface area of a sphere is 4 times the area of a great circle. A **great circle** is the edge of a **hemisphere.** A hemisphere is one half of a sphere.

Finding Surface Area of a Sphere
Find the surface area of the sphere shown in terms of π and to the nearest tenth of a unit.

6 in.

$S =$ _____   Write the formula for the surface area of a sphere.

$S = 4\pi\left(\underline{}\right)^2$ What value should you substitute for r?

$S = 4\pi\left(\underline{}\right)$ Simplify the power.

$S = \underline{}\pi$ Multiply.

$S \approx \underline{}$ in^2 Use 3.14 for π.

The surface area of a sphere with a radius of 6 in. is _____.

Holt McDougal Mathematics

SECTION 6B **Ready to Go On?**
Measurement and Geometry
SECTION B: Quiz for Lessons 3 Through 4

3 Volume of Pyramids and Cones

Find the volume of each figure to the nearest tenth.
Use 3.14 for π.

1.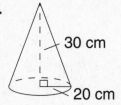
7 cm
6 cm
10 cm

2.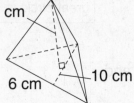
6.5 cm
4.5 cm

3.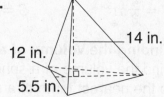
14 in.
12 in.
5.5 in.

_____   _____   _____

4.
30 cm
20 cm

5.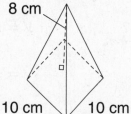
8 cm
10 cm   10 cm

6.
2.7 cm
1.8 cm

_____   _____   _____

4 Spheres

Find the surface area and volume of each sphere with the given measurements,
both in terms of π and to the nearest tenth. Use 3.14 for π.

7. radius 7 m

8. radius 1.5 cm

9. radius 2.2 ft

_____   _____   _____

10.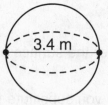
8 in

11.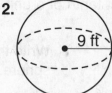
3.4 m

12.
9 ft

_____   _____   _____

Holt McDougal Mathematics

Ready to Go On?

SECTION 6B

Measurement and Geometry

Section B Enrichment: Giant Pyramids

The Pyramid of the Sun is located in the valley of Teotihuacan, 30 miles north of Mexico City, Mexico. It was built in 150 C.E. in what was then a great city. The Great Pyramid in Gizeh, Egypt, was constructed around 2500 B.C.E. It has an estimated weight of 6.5 million tons.

	Pyramid of the Sun	Great Pyramid
Height	233 ft	481 ft
Side of Base	733 ft	756 ft

1. How does the volume of the Great Pyramid compare to that of the Pyramid of the Sun?

$$\frac{\text{volume of Great Pyramid}}{\text{volume of Pyramid of the Sun}} = \underline{\hspace{1cm}}$$

_____

_____

2. The bases of both pyramids are squares. Use the information in the table to calculate the slant height of each pyramid. Use a calculator and show your work.

Pyramid of the Sun slant height = _____

Great Pyramid slant height = _____

3. If s is the side of a square pyramid and l is the slant height of each side, use the area formulas for a square and a triangle to show that the surface area of the pyramid, including the base, is $s(2l + s)$.

_____

_____

_____

4. How does the surface area of the Great Pyramid compare to that of the Pyramid of the Sun?

$$\frac{\text{surface area of the Great Pyramid}}{\text{surface area of Pyramid of the Sun}} = \underline{\hspace{1cm}}$$

_____

_____

Holt McDougal Mathematics

Ready to Go On?

Multi-Step Equations

LESSON 1

Skills Intervention: Simplifying Algebraic Expressions

If **terms** have the same variable to the same power, then they are **like terms.** Combining like terms **simplifies** an expression. **Equivalent expressions** have the same value for all values of the variables.

<table>
<tr><td>**Vocabulary**</td></tr>
<tr><td>term</td></tr>
<tr><td>like terms</td></tr>
<tr><td>simplify</td></tr>
<tr><td>equivalent
  expressions</td></tr>
</table>

Combining Like Terms to Simplify

Combine like terms. $9n + 8 - 5n + 10$

$9n + 8 - 5n + 10$	Identify like terms. _____
$9n -$ ___ $+ 8 +$ ___	Rewrite and combine coefficients of the like terms.
___$n +$ ___	What is the coefficient of n? What is the constant?

Combining Like Terms in Two-Variable Expressions

Combine like terms.

$7m + 3n^2 - m + 8n^2 - 6$

$7m + 3n^2 - m + 8n^2 - 6$	Identify like terms. Circle terms with an m-variable. Draw a square around terms with an n^2-variable.
$7m -$ ___$m + 3n^2 + 8n^2 - 6$	Rewrite with like terms together. What is the coefficient on the term m?
___$m +$ ___$n^2 - 6$	Combine the coefficients of like terms.

Using the Distributive Property to Simplify

Simplify. $3(6x + 5) - 4x + 12$

$3(6x + 5) - 4x + 12$	Simplify the parentheses using the
3 _____ $+ 3$ _____ $- 4x + 12$	_____ property.
___ $+$ ___ $- 4x + 12$	Multiply.
___ $- 4x +$ ___ $+ 12$	Rewrite with like terms together.
___$x +$ ___	Simplify. What is the coefficient of x? What is the constant?

Combining Like Terms to Solve Algebraic Equations

Solve. $7x + 2x = 81$

$7x + 2x = 81$	Circle like terms.
_____ $= 81$	Add coefficients.
$\dfrac{\_\_x}{\_\_} = \dfrac{81}{\_\_}$	Divide both sides by ____.
$x =$ ____	

© Houghton Mifflin Harcourt Publishing Company

Ready to Go On?

Multi-Step Equations

LESSON 2

Skills Intervention: Solving Multi-Step Equations

You solve an equation by isolating the variable. To isolate the variable you may have to combine like terms.

Solving Equations that Contain Like Terms

Solve.

$4x + 12 + 8x - 24 = 36$

$4x + 12 + 8x - 24 = 36$	Circle the terms that contain a variable.
$12x - 12 = 36$	Combine like terms.
_____ _____	Add _____ to each side to isolate x.
$12x =$ _____	
$\dfrac{12x}{—} = \dfrac{}{—}$	_____ each side by 12.
$x =$ _____	Simplify.

Check:

$4x + 12 + 8x - 24 = 36$	
$4(\underline{\quad}) + 12 + 8(\underline{\quad}) - 24 \overset{?}{=} 36$	What do you substitute for x? _____
$\underline{\quad} + 12 + \underline{\quad} - 24 \overset{?}{=} 36$	Simplify.
$\underline{\quad} = 36$ ✓	

Solving Equations that Contain Fractions

Solve.

$$\frac{5y}{8} + \frac{7}{8} = \frac{-3}{8}$$

$\underline{\quad} \cdot \left(\dfrac{5y}{8} + \dfrac{7}{8}\right) = \underline{\quad} \cdot \left(\dfrac{-3}{8}\right)$	Clear the denominators by multiplying both sides by _____.
$\underline{\quad}\left(\dfrac{5y}{8}\right) + \underline{\quad}\left(\dfrac{7}{8}\right) = \underline{\quad}\left(\dfrac{-3}{8}\right)$	Use the Distributive Property.
$\underline{\quad} + 7 = \underline{\quad}$	Simplify.
_____ _____	Undo the addition.
$5y =$ _____	
$\dfrac{5y}{—} = \dfrac{-10}{—}$	How do you isolate y?
	_____
$y =$ _____	Solve for y.

Holt McDougal Mathematics

LESSON 2

Multi-Step Equations

Problem Solving Intervention: Solving Multi-Step Equations

A baseball player had 243 hits. He singled 21% of the times he batted. He doubled 6% of the times and he tripled 1.5% of the times. He also hit 37 home runs. About how many times did he bat?

Understand the Problem

1. Why don't the percents add up to 100%?

_____

_____

2. What is the sum of the player's singles, doubles, triples, and home runs?

_____

Make a Plan

3. Let n be the number of times the player batted. What expression with n describes the number of times he singled? Doubled? Tripled?

_____

4. Write an equation with n to show how the different types of hits add up to 243.

_____

Solve

5. Solve the equation you wrote in Exercise 4.

_____

6. About how many times did the player bat?

_____

Look Back

7. Substitute your answer for n into the equation you solved to see if the answer checks.

_____

_____

_____

Holt McDougal Mathematics

Ready to Go On?

LESSON **Multi-Step Equations**

3 Skills Intervention: Solving Equations with Variables on Both Sides

When solving multi-step equations, combine like terms or clear fractions before isolating the variable. A **literal equation** is an equation with two or more variables.

Vocabulary
literal equation

Solving Equations with Variables on Both Sides

Solve.

A. $5a + 6 = 6a$

_____ _____   To get the variable on the same side of the equation,

$6 = a$ subtract _____ from each side.

B. $7x - 9 = 6 + 2x$ What is the first step? _____

_____ _____   Subtract $2x$ from both sides.

___$x - 9 = 6$ Combine like terms.

_____ _____   Undo the -9.

$5x =$ _____   Add.

$\dfrac{5x}{\_\_} = \dfrac{15}{\_\_}$ Isolate x.

$x =$ _____   What does x equal?

C. $2a - 6 = 2a + 8$ How do you get $2a$ to one side? _____

_____ _____   Subtract $2a$ from both sides.

$-6 = 8$ Is this a true statement? _____

There is no solution to the equation since there is no number that when substituted for the variable a, would make the equation true.

Solving Multistep Equations with Variables on Both Sides

Solve. $x + 9 + 6x = 2 + x + 1$

$7x + 9 = x + 3$ What is the first step? _____

_____ _____   Get x to one side of the equation.

___$x + 9 =$ ___   Subtract.

_____ _____   What is the next step? _____

$6x =$ _____

$\dfrac{6x}{\_\_} = \dfrac{-6}{\_\_}$ How do you isolate x? _____

$x =$ _____   Solve for x.

Holt McDougal Mathematics

LESSON 3 Multi-Step Equations

Problem Solving Intervention: Solving Equations with Variables on Both Sides

Jiffy Gym offers two plans. With Plan A, you pay a one-time membership fee of $145 and then $39 every month. With Plan B, you pay no membership fee but you pay $54 every month. After how many months does Plan A become a better deal?

Understand the Problem

1. With Plan A, how often do you pay the $145 membership fee?

_____

2. With Plan A, how much do you pay for 1 month? 2 months?

_____

3. With Plan B, how much do you pay for 1 month? 2 months?

_____

Make a Plan

4. With n as the number of months, write expressions for the cost of both plans.

_____

5. Set the two expressions from Exercise 4 equal to each other. How would solving this equation for n help you solve the problem?

_____

Solve

6. Solve the equation you wrote in Exercise 5.

_____

7. Why should the answer be a whole number of months?

_____

8. After how many months does Plan A become a better deal?

_____

Look Back

9. Complete the table to check your answer.

$n - 1$ ⟶

n ⟶

$n + 1$ ⟶

months	Plan A	Plan B

Holt McDougal Mathematics

© Houghton Mifflin Harcourt Publishing Company

Ready to Go On?

LESSON
4

Multi-Step Equations

Skills Intervention: Systems of Equations

A **system of equations** is a set of two or more equations. The **solution of a system** is a set of values that satisfy both equations.

Solving Systems of Equations

Solve the system of equations.

$y = -x + 6$	
$y = x - 2$	What are both equations equal to?____
$-x + 6 = x - 2$	Set the equations equal to each other.
_____ _____	Get x on one side of the equation.
___ = ___$x - 2$	Combine like terms.
___ = $2x$	Get the constant terms to one side of the equation.
$\dfrac{8}{\_} = \dfrac{2x}{\_}$	How do you isolate x? _____
___ = x	Solve for x.
$y = x - 2$	Choose one of the original equations to solve for y.
$y = $ ___ $- 2$	To find y, _____ 4 for x into the original equation.
$y = $ ___	

The solution to the system is (___, ___).

Solving Systems of Equations by Solving for a Variable

$2x - y = 4$
$6x + 3y = 12$

Solve each equation for y.

$2x - y = 4$	$6x + 3y = 12$
____ = $-2x + 4$	$3y = $ _____ $+ 12$
$y = $ _____	$y = $ _____ $+ 4$

_____ $+ 4 = 2x - $ ___	Set the equations equal to each other.
$4 = $ ___$x - 4$	Get x to one side of the equation.
$8 = 4x$	Add 4 to both sides.
$\dfrac{8}{\_} = \dfrac{4x}{\_}$	Divide both sides by ___.
___ = x	Solve for x.

Substitute x into either original equation: $y = 2x - 4 = 2(2) - 4 = $ ___

The solution set is (___, ___).

Holt McDougal Mathematics

LESSON 4

Multi-Step Equations

Problem Solving Intervention: Systems of Equations

Even if a system of two equations contains 3 variables, you may be able to find out something about the variables.

In this system of equations, there is only one value that x can have. What is it?

$$x + y + z = 100$$
$$x - y - z = 60$$

Understand the Problem

1. Complete and the explain why x cannot equal 30.

$(30) + y + z = 100$ $y + z =$ _____

$(30) - y - z = 60$ $y + z =$ _____

_____

Make a Plan

2. Rewrite each equation by solving for y.

$x + y + z = 100$ $y =$ _____ – _____ – _____

$x - y - z = 60$ $y = x -$ _____ – _____

3. Write an equation to show that the two expressions you wrote in Exercise 2 are equal.

_____

Solve

4. Solve the equation you wrote in Exercise 3.

_____

_____

_____

_____

_____

Look Back

5. Substitute your answer for x into the two equations and simplify. Can both equations be true?

(_____) $+ y + z = 100$ $y + z =$ _____,

(_____) $- y - z = 60$ $y + z =$ _____

_____

     Holt McDougal Mathematics

Ready to Go On?

Multi-Step Equations

SECTION A: Quiz for Lessons 1 Through 4

1 Simplifying Algebraic Expressions

Simplify.

1. $2x + 7x$

2. $6y - 5y$

3. $3p + 8q + 6p - q$

4. $3(f + 2) + f$

5. $6s - 3t + 9$

6. $5(2g - 1) - 4g$

Solve.

7. $3m + 2m = 15$

8. $10p - 7p = 18$

9. $-12z + 13z = 17$

10. $11x - x = 90$

11. $44b - 33b + 4b = 60$

12. $20s + 30s + 10s = 120$

2 Solving Multi-Step Equations

Solve.

13. $5y + 4y - 11 = 16$

14. $\dfrac{7x}{9} - \dfrac{2x}{9} = \dfrac{10}{9}$

15. $\dfrac{r}{3} - \dfrac{r}{5} = \dfrac{4}{15}$

16. $\dfrac{3b}{8} + \dfrac{b}{4} = \dfrac{5}{2}$

17. $\dfrac{1}{5}s + \dfrac{2}{3}s = 6$

18. $\dfrac{2}{3}t + 1 + \dfrac{1}{4}t = -5$

Holt McDougal Mathematics

SECTION 7A

Ready to Go On?
Multi-Step Equations

SECTION A: Quiz for Lessons 1 Through 4, continued

3 Solving Equations with Variables on Both Sides

19. $3a + 13 = 5a + 5$

_____

20. $8b + 14 = 4b + 38$

_____

21. $-3w + 4 + w = 4w + 28$

_____

22. $\frac{5}{6}x - \frac{1}{3} = x - \frac{3}{2}$

_____

23. $3x + 9y = 6m$

_____

24. $\frac{14x + y}{d} = 7$

_____

25. The pentagon and the triangle have the same perimeter. What is the measure of this perimeter?

_____

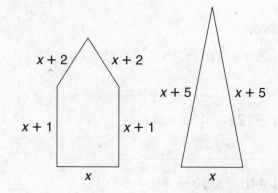

4 Systems of Equations
Solve each system of equations.

26. $y = 2x + 5$
$y = 3x + 3$

_____

27. $y = 6x - 8$
$y = 2x + 4$

_____

28. $y = 2x - 1$
$y = -2x + 3$

_____

29. $x + 3y = -4$
$-x + y = 0$

_____

30. $3x + y = 10$
$2x - y = -10$

_____

31. $3x + y = 15$
$x = -2y + 10$

_____

32. The sum of two winter temperatures is -10 degrees. Their difference is 34 degrees. Write a system of equations to describe the sum and the difference. Solve this system to find the two temperatures.

_____

_____

Multi-Step Equations

SECTION 7A

Section A Enrichment: Of Hippos and Chairs

Begin at **START**. Solve the equation in the box. Find the solution (in parentheses) in another box. Draw a line with an arrow from the box with the equation to the box with its solution. Now solve the equation in the second box and find its solution in a third box. Remember to draw a line with an arrow. Continue this way until you reach **FINISH**.

START $3x + 5x = 16$ "What"	$(x = \frac{9}{5})$ $3x + 18 = -2x + 11x - 21$ "time"	$(x = 3)$ $6x - 15 = 4x + 7$ "is"
$(x = 9)$ $\frac{11}{6}x - \frac{11}{4} = \frac{4}{3}x$ "the"	$(x = \frac{7}{2})$ $10x - 7x + 3 = 8$ "it"	$(x = 8)$ $6x - 9x = -15$ "a"
$(x = \frac{5}{3})$ $\frac{3x}{5} + \frac{4}{5} = \frac{7}{5}$ "when"	$(x = 11)$ $-3x - 1 = x - 14$ "sitting"	$(x = 5)$ $\frac{3}{4}x - \frac{3}{5}x - 3 = 0$ "chair?"
$(x = 20)$ $-3x + 2 + 4x = -4x + 11$ "It's"	$(x = \frac{13}{2})$ $\frac{3}{4}x + 13 = \frac{2}{3}x + 14$ "to"	$(x = 2)$ $5x - 2x = 30$ "time"
$(x = \frac{13}{4})$ $\frac{x}{2} - 5 - \frac{x}{8} = -2$ "in"	$(x = 7)$ $\frac{x}{3} + \frac{x}{5} = \frac{8}{5}$ "hippopotamus"	$(x = 1)$ $\frac{2x}{5} - \frac{11}{5} = \frac{3}{5}$ "a"
$(x = 12)$ $-13x + 5x = -72$ "replace"	$(x = 10)$ $7x - 3x = 14$ "is"	$(x = \frac{11}{2})$ **FINISH** "chair"

Each box on your path has a word in quotation marks in it. Write these words below in the exact order in which you came upon them.

_____

_____

Ready to Go On?

Graphing Lines

Skills Intervention: Graphing Linear Equations

A **linear equation** is an equation whose solutions fall on a line on the coordinate plane. If the equation is linear, a constant change in the x-value corresponds to a constant change in the y-value.

Vocabulary
linear equation
rate of change

Graphing Equations

Graph each equation and tell whether it is linear.

A. $y = 3x - 2$

Create a table of values.

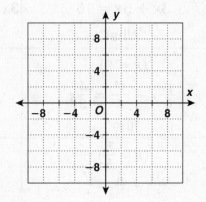

x	$3x - 2$	y	(x, y)
−2	$3(-2) - 2$	−8	$(-2, -8)$
−1	$3(\underline{\hspace{1em}}) - 2$		$(-1, \underline{\hspace{1em}})$
0	$3(\underline{\hspace{1em}}) - 2$		$(0, \underline{\hspace{1em}})$
1	$3(\underline{\hspace{1em}}) - 2$		
2	$3(\underline{\hspace{1em}}) - 2$		

Plot each coordinate pair from the table on the coordinate grid.

Does the equation form a straight line? _____

What is the change between each y-value? _____

Is the change the same between every y-value? _____

The equation $y = 3x - 2$ is a _____ equation.

B. $y = x^2 + 1$

Create a table of values.

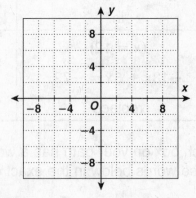

x	$x^2 + 1$	y	(x, y)
−2	$(-2)^2 + 1$	5	$(-2, 5)$
−1	$(-1)^2 + 1$		$(-1, \underline{\hspace{1em}})$
0	$(0)^2 + 1$		$(0, \underline{\hspace{1em}})$
1	$(1)^2 + 1$		
2	$(2)^2 + 1$		

Plot each coordinate pair from the table on the coordinate grid.

Does the equation form a straight line? _____

Is the change between the y-values constant? _____

The equation $y = x^2 + 1$ is _____ a linear equation.

Holt McDougal Mathematics

Name _____ Date _____ Class _____

LESSON 1

Graphing Lines

Problem Solving Intervention: Graphing Linear Equations

You can use a graph to check your solution to a linear equation.

Sara's hair grows an average of 0.4 inches per month. She just cut it to a length of 14 inches on August 1. How long will her hair be at the beginning of February if she doesn't cut it again?

Understand the Problem

1. What do you know and what you need to find?

_____

Make a Plan

2. Let *n* be the number of months since August 1. Write an expression with *n* for the number of inches Sara's hair grows. _____

3. Fill in the blanks to write an equation that shows how Sara's hair length, ℓ, depends on the number of months since August.

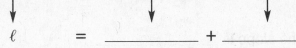

Length of hair   =   original length + amount grown

ℓ =   _____ + _____

Solve

4. To find the length of Sara's hair at the beginning of February, what value of *n* should you use? Explain.

_____

5. Use the equation you wrote in Exercise 3 to solve the problem.

_____

6. How long will Sara's hair be at the beginning of February?

_____

Look Back

7. Check your answer by making a graph and finding the value of ℓ when *n* = 6.

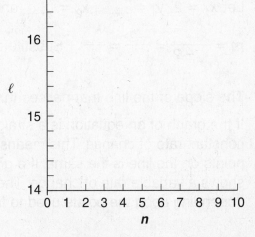

Holt McDougal Mathematics

Ready to Go On?

LESSON
2

Graphing Lines

Skills Intervention: Slope of a Line

Linear equations have a constant slope. The formula for determining

the slope between any two points is $m = \dfrac{y_2 - y_1}{x_2 - x_1}$.

Vocabulary

rise

run

slope

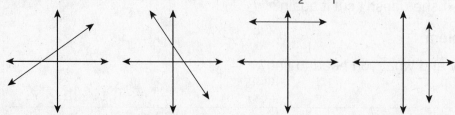

Positive slope   Negative slope   Zero slope   Undefined slope

The **rise** of a line is the difference between the *y*-values of two points on it. The **run** of a line is the difference in the *x*-values of two points on it. **Slope** is the ratio of rise to run for any two points on a line.

Finding the Slope of a Line

Find the slope of the line.

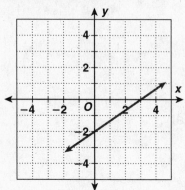

The graph is a _____.

The slope is _____.

Finding Slope, Given Two Points

Find the slope of the line that passes through (2, 4) and (8, 2).

Let $x_1 = 2$, $y_1 = $ _____, $x_2 = $ _____ and _____ $= 2$.

$m = \dfrac{2 - }{ - 2} = \dfrac{-2}{} = \dfrac{}{3}$ Substitute the values into the slope formula.

The slope of the line that passes through (2, 4) and (8, 2) is _____.

If the graph of an equation is a straight line, the graph shows a constant rate of change. This means that the slope between any two points on the line is the same. If a graph is not a straight line, it shows a variable rate of change. The slope of the graph changes, depending upon the points used to find the slope.

Holt McDougal Mathematics

Ready to Go On?

LESSON 2

Graphing Lines

Problem Solving Intervention: Slope of a Line

The points in the table are all on a line. Without graphing, find the slope of the line and tell whether it has a constant or a variable rate of change.

x	1	3	5	7
y	4	8	12	16

Understand the Problem

1. What do you know and what are you asked to find?

_____

Make a Plan

2. How can you find the slope of a line without graphing it?

_____

3. How can you tell the rate of change without graphing the line?

_____

4. What is the formula for slope?   _____

Solve

5. Use the formula from Exercise 4 to find the slope between (1, 4) and (3, 8).   _____

6. Use the formula from Exercise 4 to find the slope between (5, 12) and (7, 16).   _____

7. Are the slopes the same?   _____

8. Answer the question in the problem.

_____

Look Back

9. The equation for the line is $y = mx + 2$. Substitute the slope you found for m and any point on the line for x and y to see if your answer checks.

_____

Ready to Go On?

LESSON
3

Graphing Lines

Skills Intervention: Using Slopes and Intercepts

The **x-intercept** is where the graph crosses the *x*-axis and the **y-intercept** is where the graph crosses the *y*-axis.

Vocabulary
x-intercept
y-intercept
slope-intercept form

Finding *x*-intercepts and *y*-intercepts to Graph Linear Equations

Find the *x*-intercept and *y*-intercept of the line $4x + 5y = 20$. Use the intercepts to graph the equation.

Find the *x*-intercept. ($y = 0$)

$4x + 5y = 20$

$4x + 5(\underline{\quad}) = 20$ Substitute 0 in for *y*.

$\underline{\quad}x = 20$

$\dfrac{4x}{\underline{\quad}} = \dfrac{20}{\underline{\quad}}$ What do you divide each side by?

$x = \underline{\quad}$ Solve for *x*. The *x*-intercept is ___.

Find the *y*-intercept. ($x = 0$)

$4x + 5y = 20$

$4(\underline{\quad}) + 5y = 20$ Substitute 0 in for *x*.

$\underline{\quad}y = 20$

$\dfrac{5y}{\underline{\quad}} = \dfrac{20}{\underline{\quad}}$ What do you divide each side by?

$y = \underline{\quad}$ Solve for *y*. The *y*-intercept is ___.

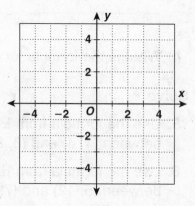

To graph the equation plot the points (___, 0) and (0, ___).

For an equation written in **slope-intercept form**, $y = mx + b$, *m* is the slope and *b* is the *y*-intercept.

Using Slope-Intercept Form to Find Slopes and *y*-intercepts

Write the equation $3y = 8x$ in slope-intercept form and then find the slope and *y*-intercept.

What is the slope-intercept form of an equation? $y = \underline{\qquad}$

$3y = 8x$

$\dfrac{3y}{\underline{\quad}} = \dfrac{8x}{\underline{\quad}}$ By what number do you divide both sides?

$y = \underline{\quad}x$ What is the slope? ___ What is the *y*-intercept? ___.

Holt McDougal Mathematics

Ready to Go On?

 LESSON 3

Graphing Lines

Problem Solving Intervention: Using Slopes and Intercepts

You can use geometric relationships to find distances on a coordinate plane.

The graph of the equation $y = \frac{3}{4}x + 3$ has an x-intercept and a y-intercept.
What is the distance between the two intercepts?

Understand the Problem

1. In what form is the equation $y = \frac{3}{4}x + 3$?

_____

2. In the equation $y = \frac{3}{4}x + 3$, what does the number $\frac{3}{4}$ tell you? What does the number 3 tell you?

_____

3. What is the x-intercept of $y = \frac{3}{4}x + 3$? Graph the equation. Label the x-intercept A and the y-intercept B.

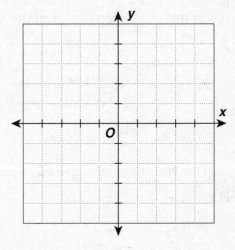

_____
_____

Make a Plan

4. $\overline{AB}$ is a side of $\triangle ABC$. What kind of triangle is $\triangle ABC$? _____

5. If you know the lengths of the two legs of a right triangle, how can you calculate the length of the third side?

_____
_____

6. What are the lengths of the two legs of $\triangle ABC$? _____

Solve

7. Use the Pythagorean Theorem to find AB.

_____
_____

Look Back

8. Make sure you graphed the equation correctly. Also, look at $\overline{AB}$ to see if it seems to be about the length you calculated.

Holt McDougal Mathematics

Graphing Lines

LESSON 4

Skills Intervention: Point-Slope Form

The **point-slope form** of a linear equation is $y - y_1 = m(x - x_1)$, where m is the slope and (x_1, y_1) is a point on the line.

Vocabulary
point-slope form

Using Point-Slope Form to Identify Information About a Line

Identify a point the line passes through and the slope of the line, given the point-slope form of the equation.

A. $y - 6 = \dfrac{3}{4}(x - 12)$

$y - \underline{\quad} = \underline{\quad}(x - \underline{\quad})$ Write the point-slope form of an equation.

What is m? ____   What is x_1? ____   What is y_1? ____

The line has slope $\dfrac{3}{4}$ and passes through the point (_____).

B. $y - 4 = 5(x + 8)$

$y - \underline{\quad} = \underline{\quad}(x - \underline{\quad})$ Write the point-slope form of an equation.

$y - 4 = 5(x - (\underline{\quad}))$ Rewrite using subtraction instead of addition.

What is m? ____   What is x_1? ____   What is y_1? ____

The line has slope ____ and passes through the point (_____).

Writing the Point-Slope Form of an Equation

Write the point-slope form of the equation with the given slope that passes through the indicated point.

A. the line with slope -3 passing through $(5, 2)$

Write the point-slope form. $y - \underline{\quad} = \underline{\quad}(x - \underline{\quad})$

Substitute in known values. $y - \underline{\quad} = \underline{\quad}(x - \underline{\quad})$

B. the line with slope 8 passing through $(-2, 6)$

Write the point-slope form. $\underline{\quad} - \underline{\quad} = \underline{\quad}(\underline{\quad} - \underline{\quad})$

Substitute in known values. $y - \underline{\quad} = \underline{\quad}(x - (\underline{\quad}))$

Rewrite the equation. $y - \underline{\quad} = \underline{\quad}(x + \underline{\quad})$

Holt McDougal Mathematics

Ready to Go On?

SECTION
8A
Graphing Lines
SECTION A: Quiz for Lessons 1 Through 4

1 Graphing Linear Equations
Graph each equation and tell whether it is linear.

1. $y = -3 + 2x$

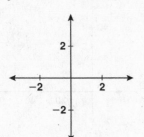

_____

2. $y = \frac{1}{2}x^2$

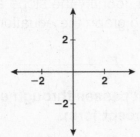

_____

3. $x = y + 4$

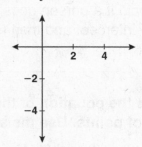

_____

4. A bookstore buys back school books according to the formula $y = \frac{1}{2}x - 5$, where x is the price you originally paid for a book and y is the amount the store will now pay you for it. What is the buy-back price for each of the books listed in the table?

Original Price	Buy-Back Price
$40	_____
$50	_____
$70	_____
$100	_____

2 Slope of a Line
Find the slope of the line that passes through each pair of points.

5. (0, 1) and (4, 3)

_____

6. (−2, 6) and (1, 3)

_____

7. (1, −9) and (3, 1)

_____

8. (4, 0) and (1, −6)

_____

9. (5, 1) and (−4, 4)

_____

10. (−4, −1) and (2, −1)

_____

11. The table shows Sam's progress during an all-day hike. Graph the data, find the slope of the line, and explain what the slope shows.

Time	Distance
3 h	9 km
4 h	12 km
5 h	15 km
7 h	21 km

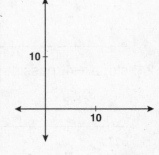

_____

_____

_____

Holt McDougal Mathematics

SECTION **Graphing Lines**

8A SECTION A: Quiz for Lessons 1 Through 4, continued

3 Using Slopes and Intercepts

12. An amusement park charges $20 to get in plus $2 for each
ride. The equation $y = 2x + 20$ represents the total amount
paid if a person goes on x rides. Identify the slope and the
y-intercept and then use them to graph the equation.

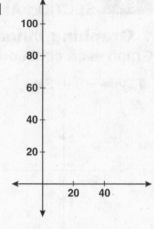

_____

**Write the equation of the line that passes through each
pair of points. Use the slope-intercept form.**

13. $(-2, -2)$ and $(4, 1)$ **14.** $(1, -5)$ and $(-2, 4)$ **15.** $(0, 1)$ and $(-3, 10)$

_____   _____   _____

16. $(-5, -3)$ and $(5, -3)$ **17.** $(-8, -2)$ and $(4, 1)$ **18.** $(3, 0)$ and $(1, 1)$

_____   _____   _____

4 Point-Slope Form

**Use the point-slope form of each equation to identify a point
the line passes through and the slope of the line.**

19. $y - 1 = 2(x - 2)$ **20.** $y = -x + 6$ **21.** $y + 3 = 4x + 2$

_____   _____   _____

_____   _____   _____

**Write the point-slope form of the equation with the given slope
that passes through the indicated point.**

22. slope 2, passing through $(1, -1)$ **23.** slope $-\frac{1}{3}$, passing through $(-1, -2)$

_____   _____

24. slope -4, passing through $(5, 0)$ **25.** slope $\frac{2}{3}$, passing through $(-6, 3)$

_____   _____

Graphing Lines
SECTION 8A

Section A Enrichment: Clown Face

For each of the following, graph the given point and draw a line with the indicated slope through the point.

1. point: (60, 110)

slope: 0

2. point: (105, 82)

slope: −2

3. point: (25, 25)

slope: −1

4. point: (82, 15)

slope: $\frac{1}{2}$

5. point: (10, 60)

slope: undefined

6. point: (38, 105)

slope: $\frac{1}{2}$

7. point: (105, 38)

slope: 2

8. point: (38, 15)

slope: $-\frac{1}{2}$

9. point: (82, 105)

slope: $-\frac{1}{2}$

10. point: (25, 95)

slope: 1

11. point: (110, 60)

slope: undefined

12. point: (15, 82)

slope: 2

13. point: (95, 95)

slope: −1

14. point: (60, 10)

slope: 0

15. point: (15, 38)

slope: −2

16. point: (95, 25)

slope: 1

Holt McDougal Mathematics

Ready to Go On?

LESSON
5
Graphing Lines

Skills Intervention: Direct Variation

If two variables are related proportionally by a constant ratio, k, then they have a **direct variation.** The ratio is called the **constant of variation.**

$$y = kx \text{ or } k = \frac{y}{x}$$

Vocabulary

direct variation

constant of variation

Determining Whether a Data Set Varies Directly
Determine whether the data set shows direct variation.

A.

Stamps	1	2	3	4	5
Price $	0.37	0.74	1.11	1.48	1.85

Make a graph of the data.

Does the line appear to be a straight line? _____

Compare the ratios. $\frac{0.37}{1} = \frac{0.74}{2} = \frac{}{3} = \frac{}{4} = \frac{}{5}$

Reduce each ratio: 0.37, 0.37, _____, _____, _____

Since the ratios are all the same this is a _____.

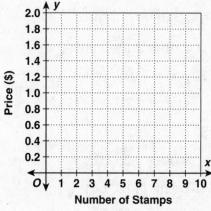

Number of Stamps

B.

x	3	4	5	6	7
y	8	7.5	6	6.5	5

Make a graph of the data.

Does the line appear to be a straight line? _____

Compare the ratios. $\frac{8}{3} = \frac{7.5}{4} = \frac{}{5} = \frac{}{6} = \frac{}{7}$

Reduce each ratio: 2.7, 1.9, _____, _____, _____

Since the ratios are _____ all the same this is not

a _____ variation.

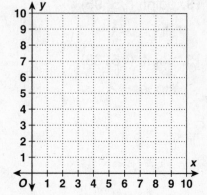

Finding Equations of Direct Variation
Find the equation of direct variation, given that y varies directly with x. y is 32 when x is 8.

$y = kx$	Write the direct variation equation.
____ $= k \cdot$ ____	Substitute for x and y.
____ $= k$	Substitute 4 back into the original equation.
$y =$ ____x	

Name _____ Date _____ Class _____

LESSON
5

Graphing Lines

Problem Solving Intervention: Direct Variation

When you travel at a constant speed, there is a direct variation between distance and time.

A driver sees a log in the road, but it takes time for her to react. During that *reaction time*, the car keeps going at the same speed. The distance the car travels before the driver brakes is the *reaction distance*. At 75 mi/h, the reaction distance is 165 ft. What is the reaction time in seconds?

Understand the Problem

1. Why does it make sense that there is a direct variation between reaction distance and speed?

_____

_____

2. Suppose the reaction time is 0.5 seconds. What would
be the reaction distance at a speed of 100 ft /s?   _____

3. How far do you travel during the actual reaction time?   _____

Make a Plan

4. How many ft/s is 75 mi/h? Hint: How many times greater is 75 mi/h than 15 mi/h?

$$15 \, \frac{mi}{h} = 22 \, \frac{ft}{s}$$

_____

5. Let t be the reaction time. Complete the proportion.

$$\frac{\text{feet}}{t \text{ seconds}} = \frac{\text{feet}}{1 \text{ second}}$$ ← speed in ft/s

Solve

6. Solve the equation you wrote in Exercise 5.

_____

_____

7. How long is the reaction time in seconds?   _____

Look Back

8. Start with your answer. See if a car would travel
165 ft in that time if its speed were 75 mi/h.

_____

_____

Holt McDougal Mathematics

Ready to Go On?

LESSON 6

Graphing Lines

Skills Intervention: Solving Systems of Linear Equations by Graphing

When you graph systems of linear equations in the coordinate plane, the solution of the system is where the lines intersect. If the lines don't intersect, the system doesn't have a solution.

Graphing a System of Linear Equations to Solve a Problem

Evan can type 30 words per minute, and Billie can type 60 words per minute. If Evan has already typed 120 words when Billie starts typing, how many minutes will it take Billie to catch up to Evan? How may words will Billie have typed?

Let t = the number of minutes.
Let w = the number of words typed.

If Evan started typing at $t = 0$, an
expression for his typing speed is:

_____

Which would make the expression for
Billie's typing speed:

_____

Graph each equation.

The point of intersection is _____.

It has taken Billie _____ minutes to

catch up with Evan. In that time she has typed _____ words.

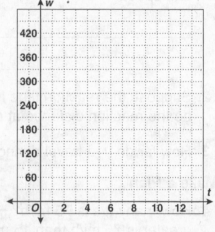

Solving Systems of Linear Equations by Graphing

Solve each linear system by graphing. Check your answer.

$x + y = 3$
$y - 2x = -3$

$y =$ _____ and $y =$ _____

Graph the two equations.

The point of intersection is _____.

Check by setting $y = y$.

_____ = _____

_____ = _____

_____ = _____

_____ = _____ ✓

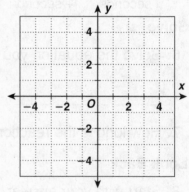

    Holt McDougal Mathematics

Ready to Go On?

LESSON	**Graphing Lines**
6	**Problem Solving Intervention: Solving Systems of Linear Equations by Graphing**

Graphing systems of equations can help you solve word problems. It takes Brenton 8 days to crochet two blankets. Holly can crochet 2 blankets in 4 days. If Holly starts crocheting when Brenton completes his first blanket, how long will it be before she has crocheted as much as he has?

Understand the Problem

1. Is the answer to the question a point of intersection? Explain.

_____

_____

Make a Plan

2. When writing your equations and graphing them, will you have Holly or Brenton begin crocheting at (0, 0)? Explain.

_____

_____

3. At what point will you have the other person when $t = 0$?

_____

Solve

4. Write an equation for Brenton's progress, and one for Holly's progress.

_____

_____

5. Graph the equations and determine

the point of intersection. _____

6. When did Holly catch up to Brenton?

_____

Look Back

7. When you set $y = y$ and plug your solution in, does your equation still hold true?

_____ = _____

_____ = _____

Holt McDougal Mathematics

Ready to Go On?

SECTION
8B **Graphing Lines**

SECTION B: Quiz for Lessons 5 Through 6

5 Direct Variation

1. The table shows how many miles Julia has traveled after riding so many hours on her bicycle. Make a graph of the data and tell whether the data sets have a direct variation.

   _____

Hours	Miles
0	0
1	9
2	18
3	27
4	36
5	45
6	54

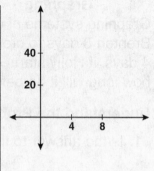

Find each equation of direct variation, given that _y_ varies directly with _x_.

2. The variable _y_ is 9 when _x_ is 3.

   _____

3. The variable _y_ is 2 when _x_ is 8.

   _____

4. The variable _y_ is 4.5 when _x_ is 4.5.

   _____

5. The variable _y_ is 5 when _x_ is 0.5

   _____

6. The variable _y_ is $\frac{7}{2}$ when _x_ is $\frac{7}{2}$.

   _____

7. The variable _y_ is 2 when _x_ is 6.

   _____

Ready to Go On?

SECTION
8B **Graphing Lines**

SECTION B: Quiz for Lessons 5 Through 6, continued

6 Solving Systems of Linear Equations by Graphing

Solve each linear system by graphing. Check your answer.

8. $2x - y = 0$
$x + y = 18$

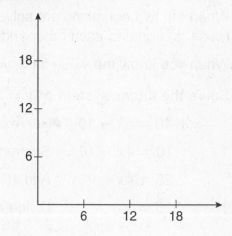

point of intersection: _____

9. $x - y = 0$
$y - x = 8$

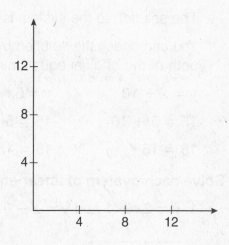

point of intersection: _____

10. The price of baseball tickets at Sunny Park and at Midnight Park has been increasing steadily since 2000. In 2000, Sunny Park was charging $3 less than the $6 they charged in '99. Sunny Park started charging $1 more each year after 2000. Midnight Park opened in 2000, and started tickets at $3. By 2006, Midnight Park was charging $9 per ticket. At what point were both parks selling baseball tickets for the same price?

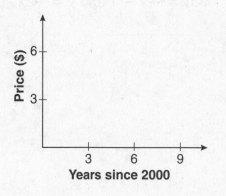

_____

_____

Ready to Go On?

| SECTION |
| 8B |

Graphing Lines

SECTION B Enrichment: Solving Systems of Equations by Substitution

A system of linear equations can be written as a single equation in one variable and you can solve the system using substitution.

When the two equations are solved for y, you can set the expressions $(mx + b)$ equal to each other and solve for x.

When you know the value for x, you can solve for y.

Solve the linear system of $y = x + 10$ and $y = 5x - 10$.

$x + 10 = 5x - 10$	Set expressions equal to each other.
$10 = 4x - 10$	Subtract x from each side of the equation.
$20 = 4x$	Add 10 to each side of the equation.
$5 = x$	Divide each side by 4.

Substitute 5 for x in either of the original equations. $y = 5 + 10$.

The solution to the system is $(5, 15)$.

You can check the solution by verifying that $(6, 15)$ satisfies both of the original equations.

$y = x + 10$	$y = 5x - 10$
$15 = 5 + 10$	$15 = 5(50 - 10)$
$15 = 15$ ✓	$15 = 15$ ✓

Solve each system of linear equations using substitution.

1. $y = 2x - 1$ and $y = x - 8$

_____

2. $y = 5x + 4$ and $y = -5x - 6$

_____

3. $y = -x - 1$ and $y = -2x - 6$

_____

4. $y = -4x + 2$ and $y = -2x$

_____

Holt McDougal Mathematics

Name _____ Class _____

LESSON 1

Data, ~~Prediction, and Linear~~ nctions

Skills Inte~~rvention~~ Scatter Plots

A **scatter plot** sho~~ws a relationship between two sets of d~~ata.
Correlation describes the relationship between the data sets.
The **line of best fit** is a line that comes closest to the most
points on the scatter plot.

Describing Correlation from Scatter Plots

A teacher studying the effects of sleep on test
scores gathered the data shown in the table. Use
the data to make a scatter plot.

Label the x- and y-axes.

Determine and fill in the scale for each axis.

How many data points do you need to plot?

_____

Plot the data from the table. For instance plot a
point at (5, 69).

Does the data appear to have a positive,
negative, or no correlation?

_____

How can you tell? _____

_____

_____

Hours Slept	Test Score	Hours Slept	Test Score
5	69	8.5	87
5	65	9	91
6	80	9	93
6.5	77	10	85
7	79	10.5	92
7	85	11	100
8	83	12	97

Test of Sleep

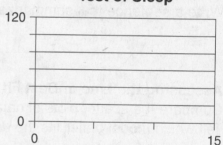

Using a Scatter Plot to Make Predictions

Make a scatter plot of the data and draw a line of best fit.
Then use the data to predict how many boxes of cookies
would be sold by someone who worked for 2 hours.

Boxes of Cookies Sold and Hours Spent Working						
Boxes of Cookies	46	50	60	50	73	75
Hours Spent Working	4	5	6	7	8	9

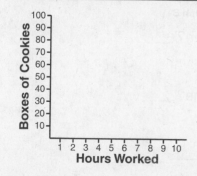

Draw a scatter plot.

Draw a line of best fit. It will have about as many points

above the line as it does _____ the line.

According to the graph, someone who works 2 hours

should sell about _____ boxes of cookies.

Holt McDougal Mathematics

Name _____   Class _____

Observe the Pattern

A study is conducted to measure the hours of sleep
the night before an exam and the score of the exam.

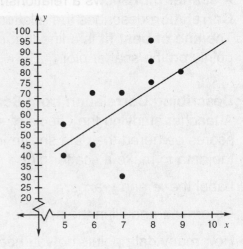

Answer these questions to describe the pattern.
Does the scatter plot appear to be linear
or non-linear? _____

Does this mean that points appear to be on a
line or not? _____

Answer these questions to identify any clusters.
Is there a location where many points are
grouped together? ____

If yes, at what locations? _____

Answer these questions to identify any outliers.
Are there any points far away from other points?

_____

Write a sentence that summarizes the pattern in the scatter plot.

_____

Assessing the Line of Best Fit

Compare the scatter plots of data and the lines of best fit shown.
Tell which model better fits the data. Explain your answer.

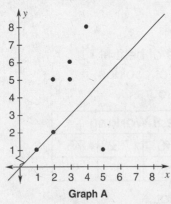

Graph A

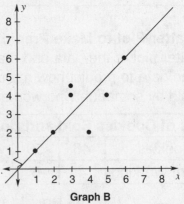

Graph B

In Graph A, do the points follow the general direction of the line? ____
Are the points close to the line? ____

In Graph B, do the points follow the general direction of the line? ____
Are the points close to the line? ____

On which graph are the most points closest to the line? _____

Ready to Go On?

SECTION 9A

Data, Prediction, and Linear Functions

SECTION A: Quiz for Lessons 1 Through 2

1 Scatter Plots

1. Use the given data of class sizes to make a scatter plot.

Year	1999	2000	2001	2002	2003	2004	2005
Class size	235	264	216	385	372	361	406

2 Linear Best Fit Models

Find an equation for the line of best fit, and tell what the slope and *y*-intercept represent in terms of the data it models.

2.

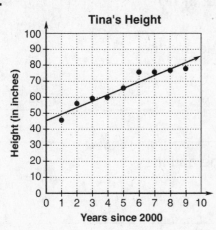

3.

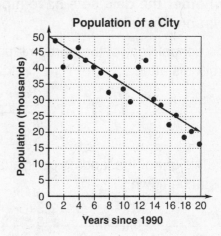

_____

_____

_____

_____

Ready to Go On?

SECTION 9A Data, Prediction, and Linear Functions

Section A Enrichment: Wingspan

A model plane contest had participants building their own planes in an attempt to travel the farthest distance. Different sized model airplanes were constructed to achieve the longest flight. The students made a table of their results.

Wingspan (in inches)	2	5	8	10	12	15	20
Flight distance (in feet)	10	16	20	24	30	36	44

1. Use the given data to make a scatter plot.

Tell whether the data sets have a positive, negative, or no correlation. Explain.

2. the school year of the person launching the airplane and the flight distance

_____

3. the weight of the landing gear attached to the plane and the distance flown

_____

_____

4. the tailwind speed and the distance traveled

_____

_____

5. Predict how far a model plan will fly if it has a 25-inch wingspan.

_____

Ready to Go On?

LESSON 3

Data, Prediction, and Linear Functions

Skills Intervention: Linear Functions

A **linear function** is the graph of a straight line. **Function notation** shows that the output of function *f* corresponds to input value *x* and is written $f(x)$.

Identifying Linear Functions

Determine whether $f(x) = \frac{1}{2}x + 3$ is linear. If so, give the slope and *y*-intercept of the function's graph.

$f(x) = \frac{1}{2}x + 3$

Graph the function.

What is the *y*-intercept? ____

What is the slope? ____

What shape is the graph? _____

The function ____ linear.

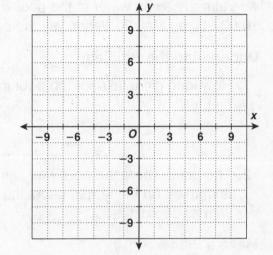

Writing the Equation for a Linear Function

Write the rule for the linear function.

What is the general form of a linear function?

_____

What is the *y*-intercept from the graph? $b =$ ____

Substitute the value of *b* into the equation. $f(x) = mx +$ ____

Use $(-2, 0)$, another point on the graph, and substitute the *x*- and *y*-values into the equation.

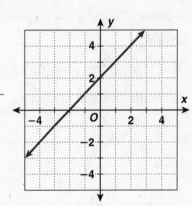

$f(x) = mx + 2$

$0 = m(-2) +$ ____   Substitute $x =$ ____ and $y =$ ____.

$0 = -2m +$ ____   Multiply.

____ $= -2m$ Isolate the variable.

$\dfrac{-2}{\underline{}} = \dfrac{-2m}{\underline{}}$ What do you divide both sides by?

____ $= m$ Solve for *m*.

Substitute the values for *m* and *b* into the function.

The rule is $f(x) =$ ____$x +$ ____.

Holt McDougal Mathematics

LESSON 3

Data, Prediction, and Linear Functions

Problem Solving Intervention: Linear Functions

Sometimes you can use graphs to estimate and then use equations to find the exact solutions.

The graph shows a 13,000-gallon swimming pool being filled at the rate of 300 gal/hr. The pool is half full at 3:15 P.M. on May 21. There was already some water in the pool when the filling started at 10:00 P.M. on May 20. When will the pool be full?

Understand the Problem

1. How long did it take for the pool to be half full?

_____

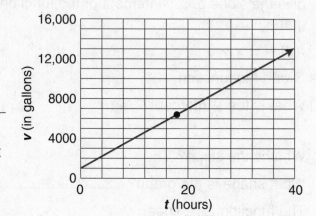

2. The point where the pool was half full is marked on the graph. Label the point with its coordinates.

Make a Plan

3. If you knew the equation of the graph, how could you find when the pool will be full?

_____

Solve

4. Find *m*, the graph's slope. _____

5. Substitute to find *b*.

$$v = m \underline{\quad} + \underline{\quad}$$

$$6500 = 300 \cdot \underline{\qquad} + \underline{\quad}$$

$$b = 1325$$

6. Find *t* when *v* = 13,000. When will the pool be full?

_____

Look Back

7. Why should it take more than $17\frac{1}{4}$ hours to fill the second half of the pool?

_____

Ready to Go On?
LESSON 4 Data, Prediction, and Linear Functions
Skills Intervention: Comparing Multiple Representations

Comparing Slopes

Find and compare the slope for the linear functions g and h.

$g(x) = 3x - 4$

x	2	3	4	5
$h(x)$	7	5	3	1

Is $g(x)$ written in slope-intercept form? _____

What is the slope-intercept form? _____

What is the slope of $g(x)$? _____

Use the slope formula to find the slope of $h(x)$.

What is the difference in y-coordinates? _____

What is the difference in x-coordinates? _____

What is the slope of $h(x)$? _____

Which function has a greater slope? _____

The slope of _____ is greater than the slope of _____.

Comparing Intercepts

Find and compare the y-intercepts for the linear functions p and q.

x	0	2	4	6
$p(x)$	3	5	7	9

$q(x) = \dfrac{3}{4}x + 2$

Does the table include a value for $p(x)$ when $x = 0$? _____

What is y-intercept of $p(x)$? _____

Is $g(x)$ written in slope-intercept form? _____

What is the slope-intercept form? _____

What is the y-intercept of $q(x)$? _____

Which function has a greater y-intercept? _____

The y-intercept of _____ is greater than the y-intercept of _____.

Holt McDougal Mathematics

| SECTION 9B | # Data, Prediction, and Linear Functions |

SECTION B: Quiz for Lessons 3 Through 4

3 Linear Functions

Determine whether each function is linear.

1. $f(x) = \dfrac{4}{7}x - \dfrac{1}{7}$ _____

2. $f(x) = 1.85x + 9$ _____

3. $f(x) = 2x^4 + 1$ _____

Write a rule for each function.

4.

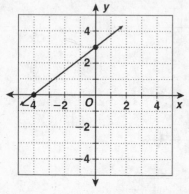

5.

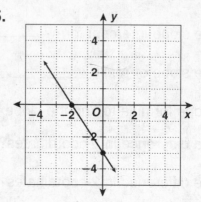

_____   _____

6. Angela has a base salary of $220 per week. She also earns a commission of $20 on every widget she sells. Find a rule for the linear function that describes Angela's weekly income if she sells x widgets. How much does Angela earn if she sells 8 widgets in one week?

_____

4 Comparing Multiple Representations

Find and compare the slopes for the linear functions f and g.

7.

x	1	2	3	4
$f(x)$	0	-2	-4	-6

and

$g(x) = -\dfrac{1}{2}x + 3$

8.

x	$f(x)$
-2	-5
-1	-2
1	4
2	7

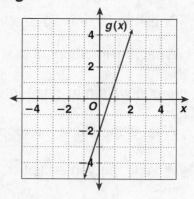

_____   _____

Ready to Go On?

SECTION 9B **Data, Prediction, and Linear Functions**

Section B Enrichment: What You Are and What You Are Not

What are you about as a person? This activity will try to answer that question for you.

First, graph each of these four linear functions.

1. $f(x) = 2x + 4$

2. $f(x) = -\frac{1}{2}x + 4$

3. $f(x) = 2x - 6$

4. $f(x) = -\frac{1}{2}x - 1$

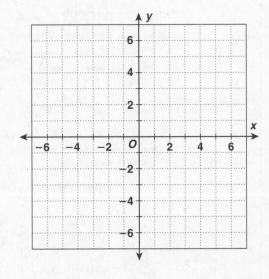

What figure is in the center? _____

This figure is telling you what you are not.

Now graph each of these five linear functions.

5. $f(x) = 3x + 3$

6. $f(x) = -3x + 3$

7. $f(x) = -\frac{2}{3}x - 1$

8. $f(x) = \frac{2}{3}x - 1$

9. $f(x) = 1$

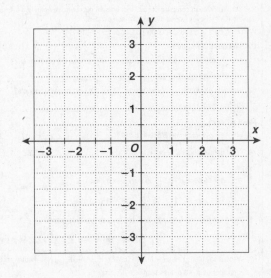

What figure is formed by the graphs you draw? _____

This figure is telling you what you are.

Holt McDougal Mathematics

LESSON 1 — Rational Numbers

Skills Intervention: Rational Numbers

A **rational number** is any number that can be written as a fraction $\frac{n}{d}$, where n and d are integers and $d \neq 0$. Repeating and terminating decimals are rational numbers. When a fraction is in simplest form, the numerator and denominator are **relatively prime.** Relatively prime numbers have no common factors other than 1.

Vocabulary
rational number
relatively prime

$\frac{6}{24} = \frac{1}{4}$ $-0.\overline{5} = -\frac{5}{9}$ $0.2 = \frac{2}{10}$

Simplifying Fractions

Write $\frac{8}{12}$ in simplest form.

$\frac{8}{12}$ What factor is common to 8 and 12? __4__

$\frac{8 \div 4}{12 \div 4}$ How do you simplify the fraction? __divide numerator and denominator by 4__

$\frac{2}{3}$ How do you know your answer is in simplest form? __The numerator and denominator are relatively prime.__

Writing Decimals as Fractions

Write each decimal as a fraction in simplest form.

A. -0.125

$-0.12\underline{5}$ Which digit is farthest to the right? __5__

What place value is the 5 in? __thousandths__

$-0.125 = \frac{-125}{1000}$ Write the decimal as a fraction.

$= \frac{-1}{8}$ __125__ is the greatest common factor of 125 and 1000.

B. $\frac{8}{3}$

Use long division to write $\frac{8}{3}$ as a decimal.

Which number is the dividend? __8__

How many times does 3 go into 8? __2__

How many times does 3 go into 20? __6__

$\frac{8}{3} = \underline{2.6\overline{6}}$

$\begin{array}{r} 2.6\overline{6} \\ 3\overline{)8.00} \\ -6 \\ \hline 20 \\ -18 \\ \hline 2 \end{array}$

LESSON 2 — Rational Numbers

Skills Intervention: Multiplying Rational Numbers

When multiplying fractions, you multiply the numerators and the denominators.

The product of two numbers with the same sign is positive.
$(+) \cdot (+) = (+)$ or $(-) \cdot (-) = (+)$

The product of two numbers with different signs is negative.
$(+) \cdot (-) = (-)$ or $(-) \cdot (+) = (-)$

Multiplying a Fraction and an Integer

Multiply. Write the answer as a mixed number in simplest form.

$-5\left(2\frac{3}{4}\right)$

$= -5\left(\frac{11}{4}\right)$ To change a mixed number to an improper fraction, __multiply__ the denominator by the whole number and __add__ the numerator.

$= -\frac{55}{4}$ To multiply a fraction and integer, __multiply__ the numerator by the integer and __multiply__ the denominator by __1__.

$= -13\frac{3}{4}$ Write the answer as a mixed number. Is the answer positive or negative? __negative__ How do you know? __The product of a negative and a positive is negative.__

Multiplying Fractions

Multiply. Write the answer in simplest form.

$\frac{-3}{5}\left(\frac{-2}{3}\right)$

$= \frac{-3 \cdot -2}{5 \cdot 3}$ To multiply fractions, __multiply__ the numerators and __multiply__ the denominators.

$= \frac{(-3)(-2)}{(5)(3)}$ Cancel out the common factors.

$= \frac{2}{5}$ Simplify. Is the answer positive or negative? __positive__

How do you know? __The product of two negatives is positive.__

LESSON 2 — Rational Numbers

Problem Solving Intervention: Multiplying Rational Numbers

You can estimate to compare products of rational numbers. You can use fractions or decimals, whichever makes the comparison simpler.

Which product is greater, $-11.09 \cdot 0.247$ or $\frac{21}{99} \cdot \left(-15\frac{15}{16}\right)$?

Understand the Problem

1. Are you asked to find the exact products? What does the problem ask?

   __no; which product is greater__

2. Without calculating, what can you tell about the sign of both products?

   __Both are negative.__

Make a Plan

3. What simple fraction is close to 0.247? $\frac{1}{4}$

4. What simple decimal is close to $\frac{21}{99}$?   0.2

Solve

5. Round -11.09 and $-15\frac{15}{16}$ to the nearest integers.

   $-11.09 \longrightarrow -11$, $-15\frac{15}{16} \longrightarrow -16$

6. Write the two products with rounded factors. Which is greater?

   $-11 \cdot \frac{1}{4} = -\frac{11}{4} = -2\frac{3}{4}$; $0.2 \cdot (-16) = -3.2$; $-11 \cdot 0.2$ is greater.

7. Without calculating either $-11.09 \cdot 0.247$ or $\frac{21}{99} \cdot \left(-15\frac{15}{16}\right)$, tell whether each product is greater than -3 or less than -3.

   $-11.09 \cdot 0.247 > -3$, $\frac{21}{99} \cdot \left(-15\frac{15}{16}\right) < -3$

8. Which product is greater, $-11.09 \cdot 0.247$ or $\frac{21}{99} \cdot \left(-15\frac{15}{16}\right)$? __$-11.09 \cdot 0.247$__

Look Back

9. On the number line, show the approximate location of the two products.

   $\frac{21}{99} \cdot \left(-15\frac{15}{16}\right)$ $-11.09 \cdot 0.247$

LESSON 3 — Rational Numbers

Skills Intervention: Dividing Rational Numbers

To divide a number by a fraction multiply by the reciprocal. The **reciprocal** of a number is found by exchanging the numerator and denominator.

Vocabulary
reciprocal

Number	Reciprocal	Product
$\frac{7}{8}$	$\frac{8}{7}$	$\frac{7}{8} \cdot \frac{8}{7} = 1$
-2, or $\frac{-2}{1}$	$\frac{1}{-2}$	$-2 \cdot \frac{1}{-2} = 1$

Dividing Fractions

Divide. Write each answer in simplest form.

A. $\frac{7}{18} \div \frac{1}{2}$

$\frac{7}{18} \div \frac{1}{2} = \frac{7}{18} \cdot \frac{2}{1}$ What is the reciprocal of $\frac{1}{2}$?

$= \frac{7 \cdot 2}{18 \cdot 1}$ How many times does 2 go into 18?

$= \frac{7}{9}$ Simplify.

B. $3\frac{1}{6} \div \frac{2}{3}$

$3\frac{1}{6} \div \frac{2}{3} = \frac{19}{6} \div \frac{2}{3}$ To write $3\frac{1}{6}$ as an improper fraction, multiply __6__ by __3__ and add the numerator 1.

$\frac{19}{6} \div \frac{2}{3} = \frac{19}{6} \cdot \frac{3}{2}$ Multiply by the reciprocal of $\frac{2}{3}$.

$= \frac{19 \cdot 3}{6 \cdot 2}$ What is the common factor? __3__

$= \frac{19}{4} = 4\frac{3}{4}$ Multiply and write as a mixed number.

Rational Numbers

LESSON 4 Skills Intervention: Adding and Subtracting with Unlike Denominators

You can add or subtract fractions with unlike denominators by first finding a common denominator. There are two methods you can use to find the common denominator.

Method 1: Multiply one denominator by the other denominator.

Method 2: Find the **least common denominator (LCD)** by finding the least common multiple of the denominators.

Adding Fractions with Unlike Denominators

Add. $\frac{3}{5} + \frac{1}{7}$

To add two fractions, you need to have a ___common denominator___.

Multiply 5×7 to get a common denominator of ___35___.

$= \frac{3}{5}\left(\frac{7}{7}\right) + \frac{1}{7}\left(\frac{5}{5}\right)$ Multiply by fractions equal to ___1___.

$= \frac{21}{35} + \frac{5}{35}$ Rewrite with common denominators.

$= \frac{26}{35}$ Add the ___numerators___ and keep the ___denominators___ the same.

Evaluating Expressions with Rational Numbers

Evaluate $n - \frac{3}{5}$ for $n = -\frac{1}{7}$.

$n - \frac{3}{5}$

$= \frac{-1}{7} - \frac{3}{5}$ Substitute $-\frac{1}{7}$ for n.

$= (-\frac{1}{7})\left(\frac{5}{5}\right) - \frac{3}{5}\left(\frac{7}{7}\right)$ Multiply by fractions equal to ___1___.

$= -\frac{5}{35} - \frac{21}{35}$ Rewrite with a common denominator.

$= -\frac{26}{35}$ Subtract. Is the answer positive or negative? ___negative___

Rational Numbers

SECTION 1A SECTION A: Quiz for Lessons 1 Through 4

1 Rational Numbers
Simplify.

1. $\frac{10}{24}$ $\frac{5}{12}$ 2. $\frac{21}{48}$ $\frac{7}{16}$ 3. $\frac{22}{77}$ $\frac{2}{7}$ 4. $\frac{13}{117}$ $\frac{1}{9}$

2 Multiplying Rational Numbers
Multiply. Write each answer in simplest form.

5. $2\left(3\frac{3}{4}\right)$ 6. $-3\frac{2}{5}\left(1\frac{7}{10}\right)$ 7. $-4\frac{3}{5}\left(-3\frac{1}{7}\right)$ 8. $\frac{8}{35}\left(-5\frac{4}{9}\right)$

$7\frac{1}{2}$ $-5\frac{39}{50}$ $14\frac{16}{35}$ $-1\frac{11}{45}$

9. Devon is making 8 loaves of bread. Each loaf of bread needs $3\frac{3}{4}$ cups of flour. How much flour does Devon need to make the bread? ___30 cups___

3 Dividing Rational Numbers
Divide. Write each answer in simplest form.

10. $\frac{4}{5} \div \frac{7}{10}$ 11. $3.2 \div 0.8$ 12. $-\frac{5}{11} \div 3$ 13. $45.62 \div 0.02$

$1\frac{1}{7}$ 4 $-\frac{5}{33}$ $2{,}281$

4 Adding and Subtracting with Unlike Denominators
Add or subtract.

14. $\frac{3}{5} + \frac{1}{4}$ 15. $2\frac{3}{7} - 1\frac{1}{2}$ 16. $\frac{22}{9} + 3\frac{5}{6}$ 17. $7\frac{2}{5} - 4\frac{1}{3}$

$\frac{17}{20}$ $\frac{13}{14}$ $6\frac{5}{18}$ $3\frac{1}{15}$

18. $1\frac{7}{10} + 2\frac{1}{8}$ 19. $3\frac{8}{9} - \frac{2}{3}$ 20. $3\frac{5}{8} + \frac{1}{2}$ 21. $2\frac{7}{8} - \frac{2}{3}$

$3\frac{33}{40}$ $3\frac{2}{9}$ $4\frac{1}{8}$ $2\frac{5}{24}$

Rational Numbers

SECTION 1A Section A Enrichment: Guess the Operation

If you are given a problem without the operation symbol, you can use number sense to help you figure out what operation was used.

A. $\frac{1}{2} \square \frac{1}{3} = 1\frac{1}{2}$

The answer is ___greater___ than the first number.

The second number is ___positive___.

So, it is not subtraction because the answer would have to be ___less___ than the first number.

What is $1\frac{1}{2}$ as an improper fraction? $\frac{3}{2}$

What is the reciprocal of the second number? ___3___

What operation uses reciprocals? ___division___

$\frac{1}{2} \boxed{\div} \frac{1}{3} = 1\frac{1}{2}$

B. $0.08 \square 0.007 = 0.00056$

The answer is ___less___ than the first number.

The second number is ___positive___.

So, it is not addition because the sum of two positives is ___greater___ than either number.

How many decimal places are in the answer? ___5___

How many in the first number? ___2___ The second? ___3___

What operation has you add the number of decimal places in each number?

___multiplication___

$0.08 \boxed{\times} 0.007 = 0.00056$

Use number sense to figure out what operation is being performed in each problem.

1. $0.25 \boxed{-} 0.5 = -0.25$ 2. $1.5 \boxed{\div} 0.3 = 5$ 3. $0.7 \boxed{+} 0.9 = 1.6$

4. $2.7 \boxed{\times} 1.11 = 2.997$ 5. $\frac{2}{5} \boxed{+} \frac{8}{5} = 2$ 6. $\frac{2}{3} \boxed{\times} \frac{1}{4} = \frac{1}{6}$

7. $\frac{3}{8} \boxed{\div} \frac{1}{2} = \frac{3}{4}$ 8. $\frac{9}{10} \boxed{-} \frac{2}{5} = \frac{1}{2}$ 9. $-0.6 \boxed{+} 0.95 = 0.35$

10. $\frac{4}{7} \boxed{\times} \frac{3}{4} = \frac{16}{21}$ 11. $\frac{7}{8} \boxed{-} \frac{1}{4} = \frac{5}{8}$ 12. $0.06 \boxed{\times} 0.03 = 0.0018$

Rational Numbers

LESSON 5 Skills Intervention: Solving Equations with Rational Numbers

You solve an equation by isolating the variable. Use inverse operations to isolate the variable.

Solving Equations with Decimals
Solve.

A. $w - 6.5 = 31$

$\underline{+6.5 \quad +6.5}$ What number should you add to both sides?

$w = 37.5$ What does w equal?

B. $\frac{x}{4.6} = 8$

$\frac{x}{4.6} \cdot \underline{4.6} = 8 \cdot (\underline{4.6})$ To isolate x, multiply both sides of the equation by ___4.6___.

$x = \underline{36.8}$ What does x equal?

What can you do to check your answer? ___Divide 36.8 by 4.6 and check to see that it equals 8.___

C. $-3.7x = 22.2$

$\frac{-3.7}{-3.7}x = \frac{22.2}{-3.7}$ What number should you divide both sides of the equation by?

$x = \underline{-6}$ What does x equal? Does the solution check?

Solving Equations with Fractions
Solve.

$x + \frac{3}{5} = \frac{6}{7}$

$x + \frac{3}{5} - \underline{\frac{3}{5}} = \frac{6}{7} - \underline{\frac{3}{5}}$ What number should you subtract from both sides of the equation?

$x = \frac{6}{7} - \frac{3}{5}$ To subtract fractions you must first find ___a common denominator___.

$x = \frac{30}{35} - \frac{21}{35}$ What is the common denominator?

$x = \frac{9}{35}$ What does x equal? Does the solution check?

LESSON 5 Rational Numbers
Problem Solving Intervention: Solving Equations with Rational Numbers

You can use equations with rational numbers to model situations and solve problems.

Kim worked from 3:30 P.M. to 7:15 P.M. on Friday and from 8:45 A.M. to 1:30 P.M. on Saturday. She earned $55.25 for the two days. How much did she earn per hour?

Understand the Problem

1. Do you have enough information to figure out how many hours Kim worked?

   yes

2. What are you trying to find out?

   the amount of money Kim earned per hour

Make a Plan

3. Let t stand for the total number of hours Kim worked on Friday and Saturday. If you know that she earned $55.25, what equation can you use to find r, her hourly rate?

   $r = \dfrac{55.25}{t}$

Solve

4. How many hours did Kim work on Friday? On Saturday? On both days together?

   $3\frac{3}{4}$ hr; $4\frac{3}{4}$ hr; $8\frac{1}{2}$ hr

5. Find Kim's hourly rate r by solving the equation you wrote for Exercise 3. (*Hint:* Use the value of t you found in Exercise 4.)

   $r = \dfrac{55.25}{8.5}$, $r = 6.5$; Kim earned $6.50 per hour.

Look Back

6. Use the value you found for r and see if Kim earned $55.25.

   _8.5 hr • $6.50/hr = $55.25_

LESSON 6 Rational Numbers
Skills Intervention: Solving Two-Step Equations

You solve an equation by isolating the variable. To isolate the variable, you may have to use more than one operation.

Solving Two-Step Equations
Solve.

A. $\dfrac{a}{3} + 7 = 15$

$\begin{aligned}\dfrac{a}{3} + 7 &= 15 \\ -7 \quad &\ -7\end{aligned}$ What is the opposite of adding 7? ___subtracting 7___

$\dfrac{a}{3} = \underline{8}$ Simplify.

$3 \cdot \dfrac{a}{3} = 8 \cdot \underline{3}$ To undo division, multiply both sides of the equation by $\underline{3}$.

$a = \underline{24}$ Solve for a.

Check:

$\dfrac{a}{3} + 7 = 15$

$\dfrac{24}{3} + 7 \overset{?}{=} 15$ What value do you substitute into the equation for a? _24_

$\underline{8} + 7 \overset{?}{=} 15$ Does the solution check? _yes_

B. $-13.6 = -3.5f - 4.5$

$\begin{aligned}-13.6 &= -3.5f - 4.5 \\ +4.5 \quad & \qquad +4.5\end{aligned}$ How do you undo -4.5? ___Add 4.5 to each side.___

$-9.1 = -3.5f$ How do you isolate f?

$\dfrac{-9.1}{-3.5} = \dfrac{-3.5f}{-3.5}$ ___Divide each side by -3.5.___

$2.6 = f$ Solve for f. Does the solution check? _yes_

C. $\dfrac{w+7}{8} = 11$

To isolate the variable, how do you clear the fraction?

$8 \cdot \dfrac{w+7}{8} = 11 \cdot 8$ ___Multiply each side by 8.___

$w + 7 = \underline{88}$ To isolate w, what is the next step?

$\begin{aligned}-7 \quad & \ -7\end{aligned}$ ___Subtract 7 from each side.___

$w = \underline{81}$ Solve for w. How do you check the solution?

___Substitute 81 in for w in the original equation and see if the equation is true.___

LESSON 6 Rational Numbers
Problem Solving Intervention: Solving Two-Step Equations

You can write equations to help solve some problems involving plane figures.

A farmer plans to build a square chicken pen from the 114 yards of fencing she has. She needs to save 20 feet of the fencing for another project. What is the longest that each side of the chicken pen can be?

Understand the Problem

1. Complete to show what you know and what you need to find.

   There are _114_ yards of fencing in all. The farmer can use all but _20_ feet.
   The shape of the pen is _square_. Find _how long each side can be_

Make a Plan

2. Why does it make sense to convert 114 yards to feet?

   The other length is given in feet.

3. Complete the equation to show how the quantities in the problem are related. Use s for the longest length in feet of each side of the pen.

   $\underline{4s} + \underline{20} = 3 \cdot \underline{114}$

Solve

4. Solve the equation you wrote in Exercise 3.

   $4s = 342 - 20$, $4s = 322$, $s = \dfrac{322}{4}$, $s = 80\frac{1}{2}$

5. What is the longest that each side of the chicken pen can be?

   $80\frac{1}{2}$ feet

Look Back

6. Use your answer to calculate how much fencing is used for the pen and the other project. See if you get 114 yards.

   Square uses 4 • 80.5, or 322 ft; 322 ft + 20 ft = 342 ft; $\dfrac{342}{3}$ or

   114 yards.

SECTION 1B Rational Numbers
SECTION B: Quiz for Lessons 5 Through 6

5 Solving Equations with Rational Numbers
Solve.

1. $x - 3.5 = 1.2$

   $x = 4.7$

2. $y + \dfrac{4}{5} = \dfrac{2}{8}$

   $y = -\dfrac{11}{20}$

3. $2t = -5.7$

   $t = -2.85$

4. $\dfrac{9}{24}h = -\dfrac{36}{8}$

   $h = -12$

5. $-9 = \dfrac{m}{2.7}$

   $m = -24.3$

6. $k - \dfrac{3}{8} = \dfrac{13}{22}$

   $k = \dfrac{85}{88}$

7. $\dfrac{s}{5.3} = 2.6$

   $s = 13.78$

8. $4.5 + p = -6.4$

   $p = -10.9$

9. $\dfrac{12}{15} = w - \dfrac{3}{5}$

   $w = 1\frac{2}{5}$

10. Joe just moved into his new apartment. It takes him $5\frac{1}{4}$ hours to paint one bedroom. His apartment has 4 bedrooms. How many hours will Joe need to paint all the bedrooms of his new apartment?

    21 hours

11. Katie and Ann are going to make cornbread for the bake sale at school. The recipe calls for $2\frac{3}{4}$ cups of cornmeal for 1 loaf of cornbread. How many cups of cornmeal will they need to make 12 loaves of cornbread?

    33 cups

12. A bag of dried cherries had 387.9 total calories. There are 4.5 servings per bag. How many calories are in each serving of dried cherries?

    86.2 calories per serving

SECTION **Rational Numbers**
1B SECTION B: Quiz for Lessons 5 Through 6, continued

6 Solving Two-Step Equations
Solve.

13. $4w - 7.5 = 2.7$

$\underline{w = 2.55}$

14. $\frac{x - 2}{4} = -3.75$

$\underline{x = -13}$

15. $5t + 5.7 = 9.2$

$\underline{t = 0.7}$

16. $\frac{s + 8}{25} = -\frac{12}{5}$

$\underline{s = -68}$

17. $-11 = \frac{m}{0.3} - 18.3$

$\underline{m = 2.19}$

18. $8h - \frac{6}{7} = \frac{2}{3}$

$\underline{h = \frac{4}{21}}$

19. $65.3 - \frac{k}{12.7} = 25.3$

$\underline{k = 508}$

20. $6.9 + 8p = -12.3$

$\underline{p = -2.4}$

21. $\frac{11}{15} = \frac{8}{35}y + \frac{3}{7}$

$\underline{y = 1\frac{1}{3}}$

22. Judy sells stamps for her grandmother. She earns $27 per week, plus $2.25 for each stamp that she sells. Last week, Judy earned $60.75. How many stamps did Judy sell that week?

$\underline{\text{15 stamps}}$

23. The local ice skating rink charges $8 for admission. Skate rental costs $5.50 per pair. On Friday night, skate rentals brought in $341. The rink made $1,333 that night. How many people went to the skating rink Friday night?

$\underline{\text{124 people}}$

24. A digital cable company charges $56.65 per month for cable and high-speed Internet service. The cable company charges $0.11 for each minute. A family's cable bill was $128.37 last month. How many total minutes did the family use high-speed Internet?

$\underline{\text{652 minutes}}$

SECTION **Rational Numbers**
1B Section B Enrichment: Combining Like Terms

When an equation has multiple terms that include a variable, you must get all the terms with variables on one side of the equation and all the numbers on the other side.

$8x + 5 = 6x - 7$ First, get all the numbers on one side of the equation.
$\underline{-5 \quad\quad -5}$ Subtract 5 from both sides.
$8x = 6x - 12$

$\underline{-6x \quad -6x}$ Now subtract 6x from both sides.
$2x = -12$ Divide both sides by 2.
$x = -6$

$8(-6) + 5 = 6(-6) -7$ Check your answer by substituting the x-value into the original equation.
$-48 + 5 = -36 - 7$ Simplify.
$-43 = -43$ The equation is true when $x = -6$.

Simplify each equation so that all the variables are on one side.

1. $7x + 4 = 2x - 8$ $\underline{5x = -12}$ **2.** $2a + 6 = 3a + 2$ $\underline{-a = -4}$

3. $6f - 3 = 12f + 4$ $\underline{-6f = 7}$ **4.** $4t + 9 = 6t + 7$ $\underline{-2t = -2}$

5. $3m - 2 = 4m + 1$ $\underline{-m = 3}$ **6.** $8r - 4 = 12r + 6$ $\underline{-4r = 10}$

7. $5j + 2 = 4j - 7$ $\underline{j = -9}$ **8.** $6w + 3 = 2w - 8$ $\underline{4w = -11}$

Solve.

9. $3y + 5 = 4y + 8$ $\underline{y = -3}$ **10.** $4b - 1 = -3b + 6$ $\underline{b = 1}$

11. $5g - 4 = 3g + 9$ $\underline{g = \frac{13}{2} \text{ or } 6\frac{1}{2}}$ **12.** $2s + 3 = 8s - 2$ $\underline{s = \frac{5}{6}}$

13. $2m - 2 = 4m + 1$ $\underline{m = -\frac{3}{2} \text{ or } -1\frac{1}{2}}$ **14.** $3s + 6 = s - 2$ $\underline{s = -4}$

15. $3k - 10 = 7k + 3$

$\underline{k = -\frac{13}{4} \text{ or } -3\frac{1}{4}}$

16. $10z + 5 = 7z - 9$

$\underline{z = -\frac{14}{3} \text{ or } -4\frac{2}{3}}$

LESSON 1 **Graphs and Functions**

Skills Intervention: Ordered Pairs

An **ordered pair** is one way to express a solution to an equation.

Vocabulary
ordered pair

Deciding Whether an Ordered Pair Is a Solution of an Equation

Determine whether this ordered pair is a solution of $y = 6x - 4$.

(3, 14) $y = 6x - 4$ What number do you substitute for x?

$14 \overset{?}{=} 6(\underline{3}) - 4$ What number do you substitute for y?

$14 \overset{?}{=} 14$ Evaluate the right side of the equation.

Is (3, 14) a solution of the equation? Why? __yes; $14 = 14$__

Creating a Table of Ordered Pair Solutions

Use the given values to make a table of solutions. $y = 2x + 2$ for $x = 0, 1, 2, 3$

Substitute each value of x into the equation. Fill in the missing values to complete the table.

x	2x + 2	y	(x, y)
0	2(0) + 2	2	(0, 2)
1	2(1) + 2	4	(1, 4)
2	2(2) + 2	6	(2, 6)
3	2(3) + 2	8	(3, 8)

Recreation Application

When renting a bike at City Park, Joe must first pay a deposit and then pay a charge per hour. If the per hour fee is $5 and the deposit is $15, then the cost c of renting the bike for h hours can be determined using the equation: $c = 5h + 15$.

A. How much will it cost Joe to rent the bike for 4 hours?

$c = 5h + 15$

$c = 5(\underline{4}) + 15$ What number do you substitute for h?

$c = \underline{35}$ Evaluate.

It will cost Joe $\underline{35}$ to rent the bike for 4 hours.

The solution can be written as (4, $\underline{35}$).

B. How much will it cost Joe to rent the bike for 6 hours?

$c = 5h + 15$

$c = 5(\underline{6}) + 15$ What number do you substitute for h?

$c = \underline{45}$ Evaluate.

It will cost Joe $\underline{45}$ to rent the bike for 6 hours.

The solution can be written as $\underline{(6, 45)}$.

LESSON 1 **Graphs and Functions**

Problem Solving Intervention: Ordered Pairs

When you use an equation to solve a problem, you can often use ordered pairs to show the solution.

The first story of a new skyscraper will be 25 feet high. Each of the other stories will be 12 feet high. The tower at the top will be 25 feet tall. If the building can be no taller than 800 feet, how many stories can there be?

Understand the Problem

1. What are the requirements for the skyscraper?

The first story and tower are each 25 feet high. Other stories are 12 feet. Total height must be 800 ft or less.

Make a Plan

2. If you write an equation relating all the given information, what variables will you use and what will they stand for?

Possible answer: h stands for the height in feet of the skyscraper and n for the number of stories above the first.

3. What value will you set h equal to? __800__

Solve

4. Using n to stand for the number of stories above the first, write an expression for the height of all the stories above the first. __$12n$__

5. Write an equation relating h, the maximum height in feet of the skyscraper, to the height of the three sections you listed in question 1.

$h = 25 + 12n + 25$

6. Solve the equation if $h = 800$, the maximum height allowed.

$n = 62.5$

Look Back

7. If n is 62.5, how many stories can there be? Explain.

62 stories; Possible explanation: You can't have half of a story, so you round down the quotient.

8. Solve the equation for $n = 62$ and show the solution as an ordered pair. __$25 + 12(62) + 25 = 794$; (62, 794)__

LESSON 2 **Graphs and Functions**

Skills Intervention: Graphing on a Coordinate Plane

A **coordinate plane** contains a horizontal number line called the **x-axis** and a vertical number line called the **y-axis**. The axes divide the coordinate plane into four **quadrants**. The point where the two axes intersect is the **origin**. The **x-coordinate** indicates movement left or right, and the **y-coordinate** indicates movement up or down.

Vocabulary
coordinate plane
x-axis
y-axis
quadrant
origin
x-coordinate
y-coordinate

Finding the Coordinates and Quadrants of Points on a Plane

Give the coordinates of each point.

A. point E

Is the point left or right of the origin? __right__

How many spaces? __3__

Is the x-coordinate positive or negative? __positive__

Is the point above or below the origin? __above__

How many spaces? __2__

Is the y-coordinate positive or negative? __positive__

What are the coordinates of point E? __(3, 2)__ What quadrant is it in? __I__

B. point F The point is __left__ of the origin __2__ spaces. The sign is __negative__.

The point is how many units below the origin? __4__

What are the coordinates of the point? __(−2, −4)__ What quadrant is it in? __III__

Finding Horizontal and Vertical Distances

Find the distance between the two points.

A. A and B

Find the absolute value of the difference of the __x__ -coordinates.

Distance = | __−6__ – __2__ |

= | __−8__ |

= __8__

B. C and D

Find the absolute value of the difference of the __y__ -coordinates.

Distance = | __2__ – __−5__ |

= | __7__ |

= __7__

LESSON 3 **Graphs and Functions**

Skills Intervention: Interpreting Graphs

You can relate both **continuous graphs**, like the ones below, and **discrete graphs**, made of unconnected points, to given descriptions by identifying key words in the descriptions.

Vocabulary
continuous graph
discrete graph

Matching Situations to Graphs

Marcy, Susie, and Ed all work at a package delivery company. The graphs below show the packages each person had left to deliver during the shift. Tell which person corresponds to which situation.

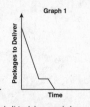
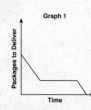

A. Marcy is new on the job. It took her nearly her entire shift to deliver all her packages, and she was given the least number of packages to deliver at the start of the day. Which graphs show someone who took almost the entire shift to deliver the packages?

__Graph 1 and Graph 3__

Which graph shows the person who starts with the least number of packages?
__Graph 1__

Marcy corresponds to which graph? __Graph 1__

B. Susie is the faster delivery person at the company. She started the day with the most packages. She stopped for a while to take a break and still managed to deliver all her packages early. Which graphs show someone who stopped delivering packages for a while?

__Graph 2 and Graph 3__

Which graph shows the person who finished early? __Graph 2__

Susie corresponds to which graph? __Graph 2__

C. Part way through Ed's shift, his delivery van broke down. He finished late in the shift because he was unable to deliver packages for half the day. Which graphs show someone who stopped delivering packages for half the day?

__Graph 3__

Ed corresponds to which graph? __Graph 3__

SECTION 2A **Graphs and Functions**

SECTION A: Quiz for Lessons 1 Through 3

1 Ordered Pairs

Determine whether each ordered pair is a solution of $y = 3x - 4$.

1. (12, 32) _yes_

2. (−4, 8) _no_

3. (1.4, 0.2) _yes_

4. (1.5, 1.5) _no_

Acme Auto Rental charges $22.50 per day plus $0.15 per mile to rent a compact car. The equation for the total cost c of the car, including mileage, is $c = 22.5 + 0.15m$, where m is the number of miles driven. Calculate the total cost to rent the car for each of the number of miles driven.

5. $m = 80$ miles _$34.50_

6. $m = 300$ miles _$67.50_

7. $m = 240$ miles _$58.50_

8. $m = 148$ miles _$44.70_

9. The Total Design T-Shirt Company has a one-time charge of $32.00 for a design and an additional $3.00 to print the design on each t-shirt. Let t represent the number of t-shirts and c represent the total cost. Write an equation that can be used to find the total cost to pick a design and have it printed on t t-shirts.

_$c = 32 + 3t$_

2 Graphing on a Coordinate Plane

Give the coordinates and quadrant number of each point.

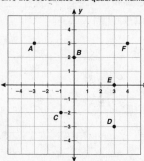

10. A _(−3, 3), II_

11. B _(0, 2), none_

12. C _(−1, −2), III_

13. D _(3, −3), IV_

14. E _(3, 0), none_

15. F _(4, 3), I_

19   **Holt McDougal Mathematics**

SECTION 2A **Graphs and Functions**

SECTION A: Quiz for Lessons 1 Through 3, continued

3 Interpreting Graphs

Tell which graph corresponds to each situation below.

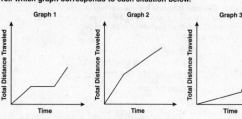

16. Rosita walks from her home to town and then rides with a friend in her car to the other side of town.

Graph 3

17. Reynaldo rides his bicycle from his home to the beginning of a path where he leaves his bike and takes a walking trip along a river.

Graph 2

18. Simon rides his bicycle to the market where he stops to buy some snacks. He then continues on his bicycle at the same pace to his grandmother's house.

Graph 1

19. Create a graph that would most likely represent the speed of an airplane as it taxis down the runway, takes off and reaches its cruising altitude.

20   **Holt McDougal Mathematics**

SECTION 2A **Graphs and Functions**

Section A Enrichment: Coordinate Plane Puzzles

Fill in the letter that names each point for the given coordinates to complete the riddle.

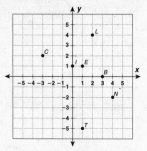

What did the zero say to the eight?

N I C E   B E L T
(4, −2) (0, 1) (−3, 2) (1, 1)   (3, 0) (1, 1) (2, 4) (1, −5)

Plot the points below. Then, connect them in the order they are listed and name the shape you form.

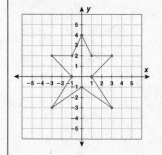

1. (0, 4)
2. (1, 2)
3. (3, 2)
4. (1, 0)
5. (3, −3)
6. (0, −1)
7. (−3, −3)
8. (−1, 0)
9. (−3, 2)
10. (−1, 2)

star

21   **Holt McDougal Mathematics**

LESSON 4 **Graphs and Functions**

Skills Intervention: Functions

A **function** is a rule that relates two quantities so that each input or x-value gives only one output or y-value. When a function is written as an equation in two variables, the **independent variable** is the input and the **dependent variable** is the output of the function. The **domain** of a relation is all its possible input values and its **range** is all its possible output values. Use the **vertical line test** to test whether a graph is a function.

Vocabulary
function
independent variable
dependent variable
domain
relation
range
vertical line test

Finding Different Representations of a Function

Make a table and graph of $y = x^2 - 1$.

Complete the table and then plot each point.

x	$x^2 - 1$	y	(x, y)
−2	$(-2)^2 - 1$	3	(−2, 3)
−1	$(-1)^2 - 1$	0	(−1, 0)
0	$(0)^2 - 1$	−1	(0, −1)
1	$(1)^2 - 1$	0	(1, 0)
2	$(2)^2 - 1$	3	(2, 3)

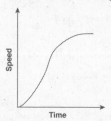

Connect the points with a smooth curve.

Does each input value have one output value? _yes_

Identifying Functions

Determine if each relation represents a function.

A.

x	y
2	4
6	8
10	12
14	16

Does each input (x) have only one output (y)? _yes_

Does the relation represent a function? _yes_

B.

What are the output values for an input (x) value of 1? _−1 and 1_

Does the relation represent a function? _no_

22   **Holt McDougal Mathematics**

LESSON 5 **Graphs and Functions**
Skills Intervention: Equations, Tables, and Graphs

You can use an equation to represent data in different ways.

Using Equations to Generate Different Representations of Data
The distance a car has traveled is represented by the equation
$d = 45h$, where d is the distance traveled and h is the number of
hours. Make a table and a graph of the equation.

h	45h	d
0	45(0)	0
1	45(_1_)	_45_
2	45(_2_)	_90_
3	45(_3_)	_135_

To find d, multiply h by 45.

What is the distance after 0 hours? _0_

After 1 hour? _45_ After 3 hours? _135_

Complete the table.

Use the information in the table to make a graph.
h represents the _input_ and d represents the _output_.
What is the x-coordinate of the first point? _0_
What is the y-coordinate of the first point? _0_
Make the graph.

Using Tables to Generate Different Representations of Data
Use the table to make a graph and write an equation.

x	2	4	6	8
y	1	2	3	4

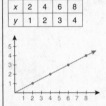

Use the data in the graph to plot points
on the graph.

What are the coordinates of the first point? (_2, 1_)

Complete the graph.
Look for a pattern in the values.
$2 \div \underline{2} = 1$ $4 \div \underline{2} = 2$
$6 \div \underline{2} = 3$ $8 \div \underline{2} = 4$
Each value of x is _divided by 2_ to get each
value of y.
Write the equation. $y = x \div 2$

LESSON 5 **Graphs and Functions**
Problem Solving Intervention: Equations, Tables, and Graphs

You can make a table and a graph to answer a word problem.

The amount of calories burned by swimming laps is represented by
the equation $c = 12s$ where c is the number of calories and s is the
number of laps. Use a table and a graph to find out how many
calories Matilda burns when she swims 8 laps.

Understand the Problem
1. What quantity are you asked to find? ___ number of calories burned
2. What do we know? ___ the equation for calories burned by swimming laps

Make a Plan
3. How can a table help?
   Sample answer: I can find different values of c for different numbers of laps.
4. Complete the table.
5. What is the first ordered pair from the table?
   _1, 12_ The second? _2, 24_
6. How can you make a graph from the data in the table?
   plot the points and connect them
7. How will the graph help you answer the question?
   Extend the graph to 8, find the corresponding value.

s	12s	c
1	12(1)	12
2	12(2)	_24_
3	12(_3_)	_36_
4	12(_4_)	_48_

Solve
8. Make a graph for the data in the table.
9. Extend the graph. What is the value of c
   when $s = 8$? _96_
10. Answer the question.
    Matilda burns 96 calories.

Look Back
11. How can you show that your answer is
    reasonable?
    Solve the equation for $s = 8$. $c = 12(8) = 96$.

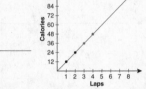

SECTION 2B **Graphs and Functions**
SECTION B: Quiz for Lessons 4 Through 5

4 Functions
Make a table and a graph for the function.

1. $y = 3x - 2$

x	3x − 2	y
−2	3(_−2_) − 2	_−8_
−1	3(_−1_) − 2	_−5_
0	3(_0_) − 2	_−2_
1	3(_1_) − 2	_1_
2	3(_2_) − 2	_4_

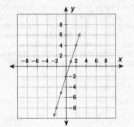

Determine if each relation represents a function.

2.

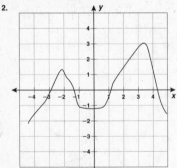

yes

3.
x	1	2	3	4
y	8	12	15	16

yes

4.
x	5	6	5	7
y	8	11	14	17

_no_

5. $y = x^2 + 2$ _yes_

6. $y = 3x + 2$ _yes_

SECTION 2B **Graphs and Functions**
SECTION B: Quiz for Lessons 4 Through 5, continued

5 Equations, Tables, and Graphs
Use each table to make a graph and write an equation.

7.
x	−1	0	1	2
y	−5	−1	3	7

$y = 4x - 1$

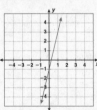

8.
x	−3	−2	−1	0
y	−3	−1	1	3

$y = 2x + 3$

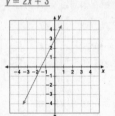

Use each graph to write an equation.

9.

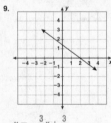

$y = -\frac{3}{4}x + \frac{3}{2}$

10.

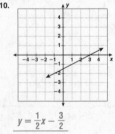

$y = \frac{1}{2}x - \frac{3}{2}$

SECTION 2B Graphs and Functions

Section B Enrichment: Using a Graph to Solve Word Problems

You can use a graph to help you answer word problems. Look at the graph below.

Does it show a positive or negative relationship? **positive**

For every unit to the right, how much does the line rise?
2 units

This amount of vertical change divided by the amount of horizontal change is called slope. It tells you what the variable in the equation of the line is multiplied by.

When $x = 0$, what does y equal? **0**

This means that there is no number added to the variable in the equation of the line.

What is the equation of this line? **$y = 2x$**

Jaqueline made this graph of her rate for doing yard work. Answer the questions below based on her graph.

1. Jaqueline has an initial charge to cover supplies for each client. What is it? **$3**

2. What is Jaqueline's hourly rate? **$3 per hour**

3. Write an equation to describe Jaqueline's rate. Use h for the number of hours and t for the total amount of money she makes. **$t = 3h + 3$**

4. Explain why the number multiplied by the variable is not 1, even though the graph looks like the line rises at a 1 to 1 ratio.

   Sample answer: The scale of the x- and y-axis are different. On the
   y-axis, one unit represents $3.

5. Jaqueline spent 2 hours weeding Mrs. Olsen's garden. Use the equation from Exercise 3 to find her pay.   **$9**

6. Jaqueline spent 3 hours working in her mother's yard. As a familiy discount, she took off the supply charge. How much did Jaqueline earn from her mother?   **$9**

7. Saturday, Jaqueline spent 2 hours mowing Mr. Harrison's lawn. Then she spent 1 hour pruning Mrs. Peterson's shrubs. Finally, she spent $1\frac{1}{2}$ hours raking leaves at Miss Ryder's house. How much did Jaqueline make on Saturday? (Each get a supply charge.)   **$22.50**

Exponents and Roots
LESSON 1 Skills Intervention: Integer Exponents

A number raised to a negative exponent equals one divided by that number raised to the opposite of the exponent.

Using a Pattern to Simplify Negative Exponents
Simplify. Write in decimal form.

10^{-2} Is the exponent positive or negative? __negative__

$10^{-2} = \frac{1}{10 \cdot 10}$ Write the reciprocal and extend the pattern.

$10^{-2} = \frac{1}{100} = \underline{0.01}$ Simplify and write the fraction as a decimal.

Simplifying Negative Exponents
Simplify.

$(-3)^{-5}$ What is the exponent? __−5__

$\frac{1}{(-3)^5}$ When an exponent is negative, write the reciprocal.

    What is the sign of the exponent, now? __positive__

$\frac{1}{-3} \cdot \frac{1}{-3} \cdot \frac{1}{-3} \cdot \frac{1}{-3} \cdot \frac{1}{-3}$ Write the product of $5 \cdot \frac{1}{-3}$.

$\frac{1}{-243}$ Simplify.

Using the Order of Operations
Simplify.

$4 - 5^0 + (7 - 5)^{-4}$

$4 - 5^0 + (\underline{2})^{-4}$ What operation do you do first?

__Simplify inside parentheses.__

What operation do you do next? __Evaluate the exponents.__

$4 - \underline{1} + \frac{1}{2^4}$ A number with 0 as an exponent equals __1__.

To change the sign of an exponent, write the __reciprocal__.

$4 - \underline{1} + \frac{1}{16}$ Simplify.

$3\frac{1}{16}$ __Add__ and __subtract__ from left to right.

Exponents and Roots
LESSON 2 Skills Intervention: Properties of Exponents

Factors of a power can be grouped in different ways giving the same product. When the powers have the same base, keep these rules in mind:
Multiply: add exponents   Divide: subtract exponents

Multiplying Powers with the Same Base
Multiply. Write the product as one power.

A. $6^4 \cdot 6^7$ Are the bases the same? __yes__

6^{4+7} What do you do to the exponents when multiplying? __add__

6^{11} Does the base change? __no__ What is the exponent? __11__

B. $t \cdot t^8$ Are the bases the same? __yes__

$t^{\underline{1}} \cdot t^8$ What is the exponent of the first t? __1__

t^{1+8} To multiply powers with the same base, what do you do with the exponents? __add__

$t^{\underline{9}}$ What is the exponent? __9__

Dividing Powers with the Same Base
Divide. Write the quotient as one power.

$\frac{10^{12}}{10^9}$ Are the bases the same? __yes__

10^{12-9} What do you do to the exponents when dividing? __subtract__

$10^{\underline{3}}$ What is the base? __10__ What is the exponent? __3__

When a power is raised to a power, multiply the exponents.

Raising a Power to a Power
Simplify.

A. $(6^3)^4$

$6^{3 \cdot 4}$ What do you do to the exponents? __multiply__

$6^{\underline{12}}$ What power is 6 raised to? __12__

B. $(9^5)^{-2}$

$9^{5 \cdot -2}$ What do you do to the exponents? __multiply__

$9^{\underline{-10}}$ What power is 9 raised to? __−10__

Exponents and Roots
LESSON 2 Problem Solving Intervention: Properties of Exponents

You can use exponents to work with very large numbers—even in your head.

It takes sunlight about 8 minutes to reach Earth. Light travels at about 186,000 miles per second. Earth is about 93 million miles from the sun. Is 8 minutes a reasonable figure?

Understand the Problem

1. How are distance, speed, and time related?

__Possible answers: Speed is distance divided by time; distance is__
__speed • time. Speed = distance divided by time.__

2. How can you figure out how far something travels if you know its speed and how long it travels? __multiply speed • time__

Make a Plan

3. Why might you use powers of ten to help solve this problem?

__The numbers are large and powers of ten can help you keep track of the__
__number of zeros in a large number. Also, you don't need to be exact to__
__determine if 8 minutes is reasonable.__

Solve

4. The speed of light in mi/sec is closest to what power of ten? __10^5__

5. How many seconds are there in 8 minutes? __480__

6. Since you rounded down the speed of light, you can round up the time. What is your answer to Exercise 5 rounded up to the next highest power of ten? __10^3__

7. Use properties of exponents to multiply the speed of light (Exercise 4) by the time in seconds it takes to reach Earth (Exercise 6). What did you just calculate?

__10^5 mi/sec • 10^3 sec = 10^8 mi; the distance from the earth to the Sun__

Look Back

8. Make sure you answer the question being asked.

__Based on speed and distance data, 8 minutes is reasonable for sunlight to__
__reach Earth.__

Exponents and Roots
LESSON 3 Skills Intervention: Scientific Notation

A shorthand way of writing large numbers as the product of a number and a power of ten is known as **scientific notation**.

Vocabulary
scientific notation

Translating Scientific Notation to Standard Notation
Write each number in standard notation.

A. 3.72×10^6

3.72×10^6 Is the exponent on 10 positive or negative? __positive__

$3.72 \times \underline{1,000,000}$ 10^6 has __6__ zeroes.

$\underline{3,720,000}$ Move the decimal point __6__ places to the __right__.

B. 2.46×10^{-3}

2.46×10^{-3} Is the exponent on 10 positive or negative? __negative__

$2.46 \times \frac{1}{\underline{1000}}$ What does 10^{-3} equal?

$2.46 \div \underline{1000}$ Divide by the reciprocal.

$\underline{0.00246}$ Move the decimal point __3__ places to the __left__.

C. -8.9×10^5

-8.9×10^5 Is the exponent on 10 positive or negative? __positive__

$-8.9 \times \underline{100,000}$ 10^5 has __5__ zeroes.

$\underline{-890,000}$ Move the decimal point __5__ places to the __right__.

Translating Standard Notation to Scientific Notation
Write 0.0000378 in scientific notation.

0.0000378

3.78   How many places do you move the decimal point to get a number between 1 and 10? __5__

$3.78 \times \underline{10}^?$ Set up scientific notation.
The decimal point needs to be moved which direction to change 3.78 to 0.0000378? __left__

Will the exponent be positive or negative? __negative__

$3.78 \times 10^{\underline{-5}}$ What is the exponent?

Check: Does $3.78 \times 10^{-5} = 3.78 \times 0.00001 = 0.0000378$? __yes__

LESSON 3 Exponents and Roots
Problem Solving Intervention: Scientific Notation

You can use scientific notation to make it easier to compare and order very small numbers.

Put the speeds in the table in order from fastest to slowest.

Event	Speed
Fingernail growth	3×10^{-4} cm/h
Growth of some lichen	10^{-10} km/h
Garden snail crawling	8×10^{-3} km/h

Understand the Problem

1. Can you conclude that fingernail growth is faster than lichen growth just because $3 \times 10^{-4} > 10^{-10}$? Explain.

   <u>No; Possible explanation: The units are different. It would be like</u>
   <u>concluding that 8 ounces is heavier than 5 pounds because $8 > 5$.</u>

Make a Plan

2. Fill in the blanks with a power of ten to convert centimeters to kilometers and then centimeters per hour to kilometers per hour.

   1 cm = <u>10^{-2}</u> m ⟶ 1 m = <u>10^{-3}</u> km

   So, 1 cm = <u>10^{-2}</u> • <u>10^{-3}</u>, or <u>10^{-5}</u> km

   3×10^{-4} cm/h = 3×10^{-4} cm/h • <u>10^{-5}</u> km/cm = $3 \times$ <u>10^{-9}</u> km/h

Solve

3. Which is faster, $3 \cdot 10^{-9}$ km/h or $1 \cdot 10^{-10}$ km/h?   <u>$3 \cdot 10^{-9}$ km/h</u>

4. Which is faster, $8 \cdot 10^{-3}$ km/h or $1 \cdot 10^{-10}$ km/h?   <u>$8 \cdot 10^{-3}$ km/h</u>

5. List the 3 speeds in order from fastest to slowest.

   <u>$8 \cdot 10^{-3}$ km/h, $3 \cdot 10^{-9}$ km/h, 10^{-10} km/h</u>

Look Back

6. Why does it make sense that when you convert from centimeters per hour to kilometers per hour, you get a smaller number?

   <u>Possible answer: In the same amount of time, you travel more</u>
   <u>centimeters than kilometers.</u>

LESSON 4 Exponents and Roots
Skills Intervention: Operating with Scientific Notation

Division with Scientific Notation
The mass of Saturn is 5.69×10^{26}. The mass of Mars is 6.42×10^{23}. About how many times greater is the mass of Saturn than the mass of Mars? Write your answer in scientific notation.

Mass of Saturn
Mass of Mars $\dfrac{5.69 \times 10^{26}}{6.42 \times 10^{23}}$

Write the ratio of the masses.

Write as a product of two fractions. $\dfrac{5.69 \times 10^{26}}{6.42 \times 10^{23}}$

Divide the coefficients. Subtract the exponents. <u>0.886×10^3</u>

Write the result in scientific notation. <u>8.86×10^2</u>

The mass of Saturn is <u>8.86×10^2</u> greater than the mass of Mars.

Multiplication with Scientific Notation
The radius of the Sun is about 1.75×10^2 times greater than the radius of Earth. The Earth's radius is about 3.95×10^6. What is the radius of Sun written in scientific notation?

radius of Sun = 1.75×10^2
3.95×10^6

Solve for the radius of the Sun.

When you cross multiply, what you quantities do you multiply?
(<u>1.75×10^2</u>)(<u>3.95×10^6</u>)

Multiply the constants. Add the exponents. <u>6.9125×10^8</u>

Write the results in scientific notation. <u>6.9125×10^8</u>

The radius of the Sun is <u>6.9125×10^8</u>

Addition and Subtraction with Scientific Notation

Add 4.67×10^9 and 3.12×10^8.

Rewrite 4.67×10^9 so that 10 has an exponent of 8.
<u>46.7×10^8</u>

Write the new addition problem <u>$46.7 \times 10^8 + 3.12 \times 10^8$</u>

Add the constants. Keep the powers unchanged. <u>4.982×10^9</u>

The constant is greater than 10, so write the result in scientific notation.

The sum is <u>4.982×10^9</u>.

SECTION 3A Exponents and Roots
SECTION A: Quiz for Lessons 1 Through 4

1 Integer Exponents
Simplify.

1. 10^{-7} <u>0.0000001</u>

2. $(-4)^{-3}$ <u>$-\dfrac{1}{64}$</u>

3. $(-3)^{-4}$ <u>$\dfrac{1}{81}$</u>

4. 8^{-1} <u>$\dfrac{1}{8}$</u>

5. $6 + 10^{-2}(-3)$ <u>5.97</u>

6. $4^{-1} + 6(4)^{-2}$ <u>$\dfrac{5}{8}$</u>

7. $-5^{-2} + 9^0$ <u>$\dfrac{24}{25}$</u>

8. $8^{-2} - (2^0 - 2^{-3})^{-1}$ <u>$-\dfrac{55}{64}$</u>

2 Properties of Exponents
Simplify each expression. Write your answer as a power.

9. $7^6 \cdot 7^5$ <u>7^{11}</u>

10. $\dfrac{12^3}{12^3}$ <u>12^0</u>

11. $\dfrac{t^8}{t^4}$ <u>t^4</u>

12. $6^5 \cdot 6^{-2}$ <u>6^3</u>

Simplify.

13. $(9^4)^{-3}$ <u>9^{-12}</u>

14. $(5^6)^0$ <u>5^0</u>

15. $(-w^6)^2$ <u>w^{12}</u>

16. $(7^{-3})^5$ <u>7^{-15}</u>

17. The hard drive on a computer holds 2^{35} bytes of data, which is 2^5 gigabytes. How many bytes is one gigabyte? <u>2^{30} bytes</u>

SECTION 3A Exponents and Roots
SECTION A: Quiz for Lessons 1 Through 4, continued

3 Scientific Notation
Write each number in scientific notation.

18. 0.000027

   <u>2.7×10^{-5}</u>

19. 115,000,000

   <u>1.15×10^8</u>

20. 0.6412

   <u>6.412×10^{-1}</u>

21. 10,000

   <u>1×10^4</u>

Write each number in standard notation.

22. 7.29×10^5

   <u>729,000</u>

23. 8×10^9

   <u>8,000,000,000</u>

24. 4.5×10^{-4}

   <u>0.00045</u>

25. 5.26×10^{-6}

   <u>0.00000526</u>

4 Operating with Scientific Notation
Perform the indicated operation. Write your answer in scientific notation.

26. $(3.6 \times 10^3) \times (4.2 \times 10^8)$ <u>1.512×10^{12}</u>

27. $(2.2 \times 10^5) \div (1.1 \times 10^3)$ <u>2.0×10^2</u>

28. $(7.35 \times 10^7) - (3.5 \times 10^5)$ <u>7.315×10^7</u>

29. $(8.12 \times 10^6) + (11.9 \times 10^4)$ <u>8.239×10^6</u>

30. $(5.75 \times 10^{11}) \times (6.8 \times 10^{21})$ <u>3.91×10^{33}</u>

31. The diameter of a rhinovirus, which causes the common cold, is 0.00000002 meter. The diameter of a human hair is 10,000 times as large as a rhinovirus. What is the diameter of a human hair? Write your answer in scientific notation.

   <u>2×10^{-4} meter</u>

Exponents and Roots

SECTION 3A Section A Enrichment: Other Number Systems

The number system used by computers is the base 2, or binary number system. This system is different from the base 10, or decimal number system, in the following ways:

• Place values are powers of 2.
• Digits are 0, 1.

1011_{binary} = 1 eight + 0 fours + 1 two + 1 one

2^3	2^2	2^1	2^0
1	0	1	1

1011_{binary} = $11_{decimal}$

$1 \times 2^3 + 0 \times 2^2 + 1 \times 2^1 + 1 \times 2^0$
8 + 0 + 2 + 1
11

To change a number in base 10 to a number in base 2, divide by powers of 2. If there is a remainder, then divide the remainder by a smaller power of 2. Continue the process until you divide by 2^0.

Change $28_{decimal}$ to base 2.

28 is between 2^4, or 16, and 2^5, or 32.

Divide by 2^4, 2^3, 2^2, 2^1, and 2^0.
$28 \div 2^4 = 28 \div 16 = $ **1** R12
$12 \div 2^3 = 12 \div 8 = $ **1** R4
$4 \div 2^2 = 4 \div 4 = $ **1** R0
$0 \div 2^1 = 0 \div 2 = $ **0** R0
$0 \div 2^0 = 0 \div 1 = $ **0** R0
$28_{decimal}$ = 11100_{binary}

Change each number in base 2 to base 10.

1. 11_{binary}
   _____**3**_{decimal}_____

2. 1010_{binary}
   _____**10**_{decimal}_____

3. 111010_{binary}
   _____**58**_{decimal}_____

Change each number in base 10 to base 2.

4. $13_{decimal}$
   1101_{binary}

5. $222_{decimal}$
   11011110_{binary}

6. $1024_{decimal}$
   10000000000_{binary}

Exponents and Roots

LESSON 5 Skills Intervention: Squares and Square Roots

Every positive number has two **square roots**, one positive and one negative. The positive square root is called the **principal square root**. A **perfect square** is a number that has integers as its square roots.

Vocabulary
square root
principal square
　root
perfect square

Perfect squares	Not perfect squares
25; 36; 196	12; 37; 186

The opposite of squaring a number is taking the square root.
$10^2 = 100$　$\sqrt{100} = 10$　$(-10)^2 = 100$　$-\sqrt{100} = -10$

Finding the Positive and Negative Square Roots of a Number
Find the two square roots of 49.

49

$\sqrt{49} = $ **7**　　What positive number multiplied by itself equals 49? **7 and 7**

$-\sqrt{49} = $ **−7**　　What negative number multiplied by itself equals 49?
　　　　　　　　　　−7 and −7

Geometry Application
The area of a square rug is 1,024 square feet. What is the length of its side?

$A = s^2$　　Use the formula for area of a square to find the side length, s.

$1,024 = s^2$　　Taking the square root of a number is the **opposite** of squaring a number.

$\sqrt{1,024} = \sqrt{s^2}$　　Find the square root of both sides.

32 ft $= s$　　What is the length of the square rug? What are the units?

Can the length of a side of the rug be negative? Explain.
　　　No, length can only be positive.

Simplify Expressions Involving Square Roots
Simplify the expression.

$3\sqrt{36} + 5$

3(**6**) + 5　　What is the square root of 36?

18 + 5　　Following the order of operations what should you do first?
　　multiply

23　　Add.

Exponents and Roots

LESSON 5 Problem Solving Intervention: Squares and Square Roots

You can solve some problems by finding square roots.

Each side of a small square gym is 17 meters long. A square classroom has half the area of the gym. How long is each side of the classroom? Round to the nearest whole number of meters.

Understand the Problem

1. If the area of the gym were 100 square meters, what would be the area of the classroom? _____**50 square meters**_____

2. If the area of the classroom were 50 square meters, about what would be the length of each side? (*Hint:* 50 is close to 49.) _____**about 7 m**_____

Make a Plan

3. How can you find the area of the gym? _____**Multiply 17 m • 17 m.**_____

4. How can you find the area of the classroom if you know the area of the gym?
   Divide the area of the gym by 2.

5. How can you find the length of a side of the classroom if you know its area?
   Find the square root of the area.

Solve

6. What is the area of the gym? Of the classroom?
   289 m²; 144.5 m²

7. Round the area of the classroom to the nearest perfect square.
   144.5 → 144

8. How long is each side of the classroom rounded to the nearest whole number? **12 m**

Look Back

9. Starting with your answer, show that the area of the gym is twice the area of the classroom.
   Area of classroom = 12², or 144 m². Area of gym = 17², or 289 m², which is about 2 × 144 m²

Exponents and Roots

LESSON 6 Skills Intervention: Estimating Square Roots

If a number is not a perfect square, you still can estimate its square root by using one of two methods:

Method 1: Use two consecutive perfect square integers that the number lies between.

Method 2: Use a calculator and round the square root to a given place.

Estimating Square Roots of Numbers
Each square root is between two consecutive integers. Name the integers.

A. $\sqrt{40}$　　What perfect squares are close to 40? **36** and **49**

$6^2 = $ **36**　　Which perfect square is less than 40? **36**

$7^2 = $ **49**　　Which perfect square is greater than 40? **49**

$\sqrt{40}$ is between the integers **6** and **7**.

B. $-\sqrt{130}$　　Which perfect squares are close to 130?
　　　　　　　121 and **144**

$(-11)^2 = $ **121**　　Which perfect square is less than 130? **121**

$(-12)^2 = $ **144**　　Which perfect square is greater than 130? **144**

$-\sqrt{130}$ is between the integers **−11** and **−12**.

Using a Calculator to Estimate the Value of a Square Root
Use a calculator to find $\sqrt{475}$. Round to the nearest tenth.

Using a calculator, $\sqrt{475} \approx 21.7$ **94494** ...

What is 21.794494 rounded to the nearest tenth? **21.8**

LESSON 6 Exponents and Roots
Problem Solving Intervention: Estimating Square Roots

If you drop a penny, the time it takes to hit the ground depends on the height from which you drop it. If you know h, the height in feet, and if you ignore the effect of air, you can use a formula to find t, the number of seconds it takes to fall.

$$t = \sqrt{\frac{2h}{32}}$$

How many times longer will it take a penny to drop from 576 feet than from 144 feet?

Understand the Problem

1. How long would it take a penny to drop from a height of 16 feet? __1 second__

2. What are you being asked to compare?

   __the time it takes from 576 feet and the time it takes from 144 feet__

Make a Plan

3. How can you find the two times?

   __Substitute 576 for h and then substitute 144 for h.__

4. Will you subtract or divide to compare? Why?

   __Divide; The problem asks "How many times longer?" not "How many__
   __seconds longer?"__

Solve

5. How long will it take the penny to fall from 576 feet? From 144 feet?

   __6 seconds; 3 seconds__

6. How many times longer will it take? __2 times longer__

Look Back

7. If you square both sides of the formula, you get $t^2 = \frac{2d}{32}$. Use that to check your values of t and h.

   $(3)^2 = \frac{2(144)}{32}$, $9 = \frac{288}{32}$, $9 = 9$

   $(6)^2 = \frac{2(576)}{32}$, $36 = \frac{1152}{32}$, $36 = 36$

LESSON 7 Exponents and Roots
Skills Intervention: The Real Numbers

Real numbers consist of the set of rational numbers and **irrational numbers**. Irrational numbers are non-terminating, non-repeating decimals.

Vocabulary
real number
irrational number
Density Property

Real Numbers

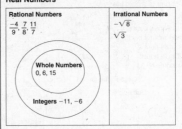

Rational Numbers	Irrational Numbers
$\frac{-4}{9}$, $\frac{7}{8}$, $\frac{11}{7}$	$-\sqrt{8}$ $\sqrt{3}$

Whole Numbers 0, 6, 15

Integers -11, -6

Classifying Real Numbers
Write all names that apply to each number.

A. $\sqrt{13}$

Is 13 a perfect square? __no__

Classify $\sqrt{13}$. __irrational, real__

B. -21.78

Is -21.78 a terminating or repeating decimal? __terminating__

Is -21.78 a rational number or irrational number? __rational number__

Classify -21.78. __real, rational__

The **Density Property** of real numbers states that between any two real numbers is another real number.

Applying the Density Property of Real Numbers

Find a real number between $1\frac{1}{5}$ and $1\frac{2}{5}$.

One of the many solutions is the number halfway between the two numbers.

$\left(1\frac{1}{5} + 1\frac{2}{5}\right) \div 2$ Add the numbers.

$\left(2\boxed{\frac{3}{5}}\right) \div 2 = \underline{1\frac{3}{10}}$ Divide by 2.

A number between $1\frac{1}{5}$ and $1\frac{2}{5}$ is $\underline{1\frac{3}{10}}$.

LESSON 8 Exponents and Roots
Skills Intervention: The Pythagorean Theorem

The **Pythagorean Theorem** states that in a right triangle, the sum of the squares of the lengths of the two **legs** is equal to the square of the length of the **hypotenuse**.

$a^2 + b^2 = c^2$

Vocabulary
Pythagorean Theorem
leg
hypotenuse

Finding the Length of a Hypotenuse
Find the length of the hypotenuse.

$\underline{a^2 + b^2} = c^2$	Write the Pythagorean Theorem.
$2^2 + 2^2 = c^2$	Substitute $\underline{2}$ for a and $\underline{2}$ for b.
$4 + 4 = c^2$	Simplify.
$\sqrt{8} = c$	How do you isolate c?
	__Take the square root of both sides.__
$\underline{2.83} \approx c$	Use a calculator.

Finding the Length of a Leg in a Right Triangle
Solve for the unknown side in the right triangle.

$6^2 + b^2 = \underline{10^2}$	Substitute values for a and c.
$36 + b^2 = 100$	Simplify.
$b^2 = \underline{64}$	Isolate the variable.
$b = \sqrt{64}$	Take the square root of both sides.
$b = \underline{8}$	The length of the unknown leg is $\underline{8}$.

Using the Pythagorean Theorem for Measurement
Sam and Julia go to the same school. Sam lives 3 miles south of the school. Julia lives 6 miles west of the school. How far apart do Sam and Julia live from each other?

Julia's Home   6 mi   School

3 mi

Sam's Home

The distance Sam and Julia live from each other is the hypotenuse of a right triangle.

$a^2 + b^2 = c^2$	State the Pythagorean Theorem.
$\underline{3}^2 + \underline{6}^2 = c^2$	Substitute values for a and b.
$\underline{9} + \underline{36} = c^2$	Simplify.
$\underline{45} = c^2$	Add.
$\sqrt{45} = c$	Take the square root of both sides.
$\underline{6.7} \approx c$	Use a calculator. Round to the nearest tenth.

Sam and Julia live $\underline{6.7}$ miles apart from each other.

LESSON 8 Exponents and Roots
Problem Solving Intervention: The Pythagorean Theorem

You can use the Pythagorean Theorem to help you find an unknown measurement.

A rectangular park is 240 feet long and 180 feet wide. What is the length of a diagonal path that connects two corners of the park?

240 ft

180 ft

Understand the Problem

1. Draw a diagram of the park. Label the side lengths. Show the diagonal path on your diagram.

2. What kind of triangles are formed by the diagonal and the sides of the park? __right triangles__

Make a Plan

3. How does the Pythagorean Theorem relate the sides lengths of a right triangle?

   __The sum of the squares of the legs equals the square of the hypotenuse.__

4. What equation states the Pythagorean Theorem? __$a^2 + b^2 = c^2$__

5. How can you use this equation to solve the problem?

   __Substitute the lengths of the legs for a and b and solve for c.__

Solve

6. Substitute the values into in the Pythagorean Theorem. __$240^2 + 180^2 = c^2$__

7. Solve for c. Use your calculator. __$c = 300$__

8. How long is the diagonal path? __300 feet__

Look Back

9. Is your answer reasonable? Explain.

   __Possible answer: Yes; The diagonal path is the hypotenuse of a right__
   __triangle with sides of 240 ft and 180 ft, so it must be longer than 240 ft.__
   __The third side of a triangle cannot be longer than the sum of the other two__
   __sides. 300 < 240 + 180, or 420.__

© Houghton Mifflin Harcourt Publishing Company

LESSON 9 — Exponents and Roots
Skills Intervention: Applying the Pythagorean Theorem and Its Converse

You can use the Pythagorean Theorem to solve problems about lengths and distances in right triangles. The converse of the Pythagorean theorem states that if a triangle has side lengths a, b, and c, and $a^2 + b^2 = c^2$, then the triangle is a right triangle.

Fitness Application
For exercise, Keisha walks 1.8 km to Alice's house, then 0.7 km to Tino's house, and then returns back home. If the 3 streets on the map form a right triangle, what is the distance from Tino's house to Keisha's house, to the nearest hundredth?

Tino's House
0.7 km
Alice's House   1.8 km   Keisha's House

$a^2 + b^2 = c^2$	Use the Pythagorean Theorem.
$\underline{1.8}\,^2 + \underline{0.7}\,^2 = c^2$	Substitute.
$\underline{3.24} + \underline{0.49} = c^2$	Multiply.
$\underline{3.73} = c^2$	Add.
$\sqrt{3.73} = c^2$	Find the square root.
$\underline{1.93} \cong c$	

The distance from Tino's to Keisha's is about $\underline{1.93}$ kilometers.

Identifying a Right Triangle
Tell whether the given side lengths form a right triangle.

A. 18, 80, 82

$a^2 + b^2 \overset{?}{=} c^2$	Compare $a^2 + b^2 = c^2$.
$\underline{18}\,^2 + \underline{80}\,^2 \overset{?}{=} \underline{82}\,^2$	Substitute.
$\underline{324} + \underline{6,400} \overset{?}{=} 6,724$	Simplify.
$\underline{6,724} = 6,724$	Add.

Do the side lengths for a right triangle? $\underline{yes}$

B. 7, 25, 26

$a^2 + b^2 \overset{?}{=} c^2$	Compare $a^2 + b^2 = c^2$.
$\underline{7}\,^2 + \underline{25}\,^2 \overset{?}{=} \underline{26}\,^2$	Substitute.
$\underline{49} + \underline{625} \overset{?}{=} 676$	Simplify.
$\underline{674} \neq 676$	Add.

Do the side lengths for a right triangle? $\underline{no}$

SECTION 3B — Exponents and Roots
SECTION B: Quiz for Lessons 5 Through 9

5 Squares and Square Roots
Find the two square roots of each number.

1. 64   **2.** 6,084   **3.** 1,000,000   **4.** 324

$\underline{8;\ -8}$ $\underline{78;\ -78}$ $\underline{1,000;\ -1,000}$ $\underline{18;\ -18}$

5. Amy wants to put together a jigsaw puzzle that will be 24 in. × 20 in. when finished. Will the puzzle fit on a square board with an area of 529 square inches? Explain your answer.

$\underline{No;\ \sqrt{529} = 23,\ \text{so the board is 23 in.} \times 23\ \text{in. One dimension is}}$
$\underline{\text{not long enough for the puzzle.}}$

6. How many 6 in. × 6 in. square tiles will fit around the edges of a square hallway that has an area of 1,296 square inches? $\underline{24}$

6 Estimating Square Roots
Each square root is between two integers. Name the integers. Explain your answer.

7. $-\sqrt{56}$

$\underline{-7\ \text{and}\ -8;\ 56\ \text{is between}}$
$\underline{49\ \text{and}\ 64}$

8. $\sqrt{300}$

$\underline{17\ \text{and}\ 18;\ 300\ \text{is between}}$
$\underline{289\ \text{and}\ 324}$

9. $-\sqrt{250}$

$\underline{-15\ \text{and}\ -16;\ 250\ \text{is between}}$
$\underline{225\ \text{and}\ 256}$

10. $\sqrt{860}$

$\underline{29\ \text{and}\ 30;\ 860\ \text{is between}}$
$\underline{841\ \text{and}\ 900}$

11. A square quilt has an area of 28 square feet. To the nearest hundredth, what length of edging is needed to go around all the edges of the quilt? $\underline{21.16\ feet}$

12. The area of a square painting is 120 square inches. Find the length of one side of the painting to the nearest hundredth. $\underline{10.95\ inches}$

SECTION 3B — Exponents and Roots
SECTION B: Quiz for Lessons 5 Through 9, continued

7 The Real Numbers
Write all the names that apply to each number.

13. 0.26   **14.** $\sqrt{35}$

$\underline{rational,\ real}$ $\underline{irrational,\ real}$

15. $\sqrt{400}$ **16.** $\dfrac{-\sqrt{100}}{5}$

$\underline{whole,\ integer,\ rational,\ real}$ $\underline{whole,\ integer,\ rational,\ real}$

17. Find a real number between $\sqrt{49}$ and 8. $\underline{\text{Possible answer: 7.6}}$

8 The Pythagorean Theorem
Find the missing length for each right triangle. Round your answer to the nearest tenth.

18. $a = 6$, $b = 10$, $c = ?$ **19.** $a = 4$, $b = ?$, $c = 12$

$\underline{11.7}$ $\underline{11.3}$

20. $a = ?$, $b = 15$, $c = 17$ **21.** $a = 36$, $b = 48$, $c = ?$

$\underline{8}$ $\underline{60}$

22. Jason is putting a fence around a garden. The measures of two sides that meet at a corner are 25 feet and 38 feet. For the corner to be a right angle, what would the length of the diagonal have to be? $\underline{\approx 45.5\ feet}$

9 Applying the Pythagorean Theorem and Its Converse
Tell whether the given side lengths form a right triangle.

23. 8, 15, 17   **24.** 3, 6, 7

$\underline{yes}$ $\underline{no}$

25. 13, 24, 25   **26.** 11, 60, 61

$\underline{no}$ $\underline{yes}$

27. Nila folds a 8.5 in × 11 in sheet of paper along the diagonal. To the nearest tenth, what is the length of the diagonal? $\underline{13.9\ inches}$

SECTION 3B — Exponents and Roots
Section B Enrichment: Proving the Pythagorean Theorem

It has been said that the Pythagorean Theorem has been proven to be true in more ways than any other theorem in mathematics. Use the diagram and complete the steps to complete one of these proofs.

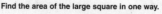

Find the area of the large square in one way.

1. Use the variables a and b to represent the length of one side of the large square.
$\underline{a + b}$

2. Use Step 1 to write the area of the large square. $\underline{(a + b)(a + b)}$

3. Apply the Distributive Property to the expression in Step 2. Use exponents.
$(a + b)(a + b) = a^2 + \underline{ab} + \underline{ba} + \underline{b^2}$

4. Simplify the expression in Step 3. Remember that ab and ba represent the same quantity. $\underline{a^2 + 2ab + b^2}$

Find the area of the large square in another way.

5. The area of the large square equals the area of $\underline{\text{the small}}$ $\underline{\text{square}}$ plus the area of $\underline{\text{the 4 triangles}}$.

6. Use the variable c to represent the area of the small square. $\underline{c^2}$

7. Use the formula for the area of a triangle and the variables a and b to write the area of one triangle. $\underline{\tfrac{1}{2}ab}$

8. Use Steps 6 and 7 to write the area of the large square. $\underline{c^2 + 4\left(\tfrac{1}{2}ab\right)}$

9. Simplify the expression in Step 8. $\underline{c^2 + 2ab}$

10. Use Steps 4 and 9. Write an equation to show that the two expressions for the area of the large square are equal. $\underline{a^2 + 2ab + b^2 = c^2 + 2ab}$

11. Subtract the quantity that is the same from both sides of the equation in Step 10. $\underline{a^2 + b^2 = c^2}$

12. How does the equation in Step 11 compare to the Pythagorean Theorem?

$\underline{\text{It is the same.}}$

LESSON 1 · Ratios, Proportions, and Similarity
Skills Intervention: Ratios, Rates, and Unit Rates

A comparison of two quantities that have different units is a **rate**.
Unit rates are simplified rates in which the second quantity is one.
Unit price is a unit rate that compares the cost of item units.

Vocabulary
rate
unit rate
unit price

Finding Unit Rates

Alison can read 6 pages in 15 minutes. How many pages can she read in 1 hour?

$\dfrac{6 \text{ pages}}{15 \text{ minutes}}$ Write the information as a rate.

$\dfrac{6 \text{ pages} \times 4}{15 \text{ minutes} \times 4} = \dfrac{24 \text{ pages}}{60 \text{ minutes}}$ How many minutes do you want in the proportional rate? __60__

$= \dfrac{24 \text{ pages}}{1 \text{ hour}}$ Alison can read __24__ pages in 1 hour.

Science Application

Gold weighing 193 kg has a volume of 0.01 m³. What is the density of gold?

$\dfrac{193 \text{ kg}}{0.01 \text{ m}^3}$ Write the rate.

$\dfrac{193 \text{ kg} \times 100}{0.01 \text{ m}^3 \times 100} = \dfrac{19{,}300 \text{ kg}}{1 \text{ m}^3}$ Multiply to find kilograms per 1 m³.

Gold has a density of __19,300__ kg/m³.

Travel Application

Jessie drives 203 miles in 3.5 hours. What is his average rate of speed?

$\dfrac{203 \text{ miles}}{3.5 \text{ hours}}$ Write the rate.

$\dfrac{203 \text{ miles} \div 3.5}{3.5 \text{ hours} \div 3.5} = \dfrac{58 \text{ miles}}{1 \text{ hour}}$ Divide to find miles per 1 hour.

Jessie's rate of speed is __58 miles__ per __hour__.

Finding Unit Prices to Compare Costs

A 14-oz box of cereal cost $3.29 and a 20-oz box of the same cereal cost $4.19. Which is the better buy?

To find the unit rate, divide the __price__ by the __number of ounces__.

$\dfrac{\text{price of box \#1}}{\text{number of ounces}} = \dfrac{\$3.29}{14} = \$0.235$ $\dfrac{\text{price of box \#2}}{\text{number of ounces}} = \dfrac{\$4.19}{20} = \$0.2095$

In which box are you paying less per ounce? __20 oz box__

Is the smaller or the larger box a better buy? __larger__

LESSON 1 · Ratios, Proportions, and Similarity
Problem Solving Intervention: Ratios, Rates, and Unit Rates

For $7.29 you can buy a pack of 8 AA batteries that comes with an additional free battery. Or you can buy a pack of 4 AA batteries for $2.89. Which costs less per battery? Explain.

Understand the Problem

1. How many batteries do you get in the package that costs $7.29? __9__

Make a Plan

2. What two ratios can you compare to solve the problem?

Sample answer: $\dfrac{\$7.29}{9}$ and $\dfrac{\$2.89}{4}$

3. Suppose you knew the cost of 36 batteries when purchased in the 8-packs. Suppose you also knew the cost of 36 batteries when purchased in the 4-packs. How would that help you? Why is 36 a convenient number to use for this comparison?

Whichever costs less for 36 batteries would also cost less for 1 battery.

36 is a common multiple of 4 and 9, so you can just multiply to find out

how much 36 batteries would cost.

Solve

4. How many of the $7.29 packs would you need in order to get 36 batteries? What would you multiply to find how much that would cost?

4; 4 • $7.29

5. How many of the $2.89 packs would you need in order to get 36 batteries? What would you multiply to find how much that would cost?

9; 9 • $2.89

6. Estimate. Is 4 • $7.29 greater than or less than $28? Is 9 • $2.89 greater than or less than $28? Explain.

4 • $7.29 > $28 because it's greater than 4 • $7.

9 • $2.89 < $28 because it's less than 9 • $3.

Look Back

7. Make sure you answer the question and explain your answer.

The $2.89 pack costs less per battery. It costs less than $28 for 36

batteries. The other costs more than $28 for 36 batteries.

LESSON 2 · Ratios, Proportions, and Similarity
Skills Intervention: Solving Proportions

Cross products in proportions are equal. If the cross products are not equal then the ratios are not in proportion.

Vocabulary
cross products

Using Cross Products to Identify Proportions

Tell whether the ratios are proportional.

A. $\dfrac{10}{32} = \dfrac{8}{28}$ B. $\dfrac{15}{25} = \dfrac{6}{10}$

$\dfrac{10}{32} \diagup\!\!\!\!\diagdown \dfrac{8}{28}$ Find cross products. $\dfrac{15}{25} \diagup\!\!\!\!\diagdown \dfrac{6}{10}$ Find cross products.

$10 \times 28 = 280$ $15 \times 10 = 150$

$32 \times 8 = 256$ $25 \times 6 = 150$

Are the cross products equal? __no__   Are the cross products equal? __yes__

Are the ratios proportional? __no__   Are the ratios proportional? __yes__

C. A bottle of liquid lawn fertilizer instructs you to mix one part fertilizer and 16 parts water. Is a mixture of 68 oz of water and 4 oz of fertilizer proportional to this ratio?

What is the fertilizer to water ratio given on the bottle? $\dfrac{1}{16}$

What is the fertilizer to water ratio of the mixture? $\dfrac{4}{68}$

$\dfrac{1}{16} = \dfrac{4}{68}$ What are the cross products? __68 and 64__

          Are they equal? __no__

          Is this a correct mixture of fertilizer? __no__

Using Cross Products to Solve Proportions

Carla has driven her car 13.6 miles in 12 minutes. At this rate, how far can Carla drive in 3 hours?

$\dfrac{13.6}{12} = \dfrac{d}{180}$ Set up a proportion. Use d for the unknown distance.

$13.6 • \underline{180} = \underline{12} • d$ Find the cross products.

$\underline{2{,}448} = 12d$ Multiply.

$\dfrac{2{,}448}{12} = \dfrac{12d}{12}$ Divide both sides by __12__.

$\underline{204} = d$

Carla can drive __204__ miles in 3 hours.

LESSON 2 · Ratios, Proportions, and Similarity
Problem Solving Intervention: Solving Proportions

You can write and solve proportions to see what will happen if a rate continues.

At 2:10 P.M., your family began a 58-mile car trip to Grandma's. At 2:50 P.M., you have gone 23 miles. At this rate, will you get there by 3:30 P.M.?

Understand the Problem

1. How many miles is the whole trip to Grandma's? How many miles have you driven so far?

58 miles; 23 miles

2. Do you have to find the exact time of arrival?

No; only if you will get there by 3:30.

3. If you arrive at 3:30, how long will the whole trip have taken?

1 hour and 20 minutes, or 80 minutes

Make a Plan

4. Let x be the number of minutes it takes for the whole trip. What must x be less than or equal to for you to arrive in time? __80__

5. Complete the proportion to show how you could find x.

$\dfrac{23 \text{ miles}}{40 \text{ minutes}} = \dfrac{58 \text{ miles}}{x \text{ minutes}}$

6. Why can you estimate or use mental math to solve the problem?

Sample answer: You don't need to find an exact amount, just if $x < 80$.

Solve

7. Is 58 miles greater than or less than 2 times 23 miles?

greater than

8. Why must x be more than 80?

Since $58 > 2 • 23$, $x > 2 • 40$.

Look Back

9. Make sure you answer the question that the problem asks.

No, at that rate I won't make it by 3:30.

Ratios, Proportions, and Similarity
SECTION 4A SECTION A: Quiz for Lessons 1 Through 2

1 Ratios, Rates, and Unit Rates

1. The mass of a chunk of titanium is 55 g. The volume is 12.5 cm^3. What is the density of the chunk of titanium? **4.4 g/ cm^3**

2. Bixbyite is a rare mineral with a density of 4.95 g/cm^3. What is the volume of a piece of bixbyite with a mass of 101.97 g? **20.6 cm^3**

3. Maria's St. Bernard, Arfy, is fed the same amount of food every day. If Arfy gets fed 36.75 cups of dog food per week, how many cups of dog food does he get fed per day? **5.25 cups**

Determine the better buy.

4. 40 lb of potatoes for $11.20 or 60 lb of potatoes for $16.20 **60 lb**

5. $35.70 for 15 gallons of gas or $64.80 for 27 gallons of gas **15 gal**

2 Solving Proportions
Solve each proportion.

6. $\frac{12,000 \text{ tons}}{8 \text{ weeks}} = \frac{t \text{ tons}}{22 \text{ weeks}}$ **33,000 t**

7. $\frac{440 \text{ meters}}{32 \text{ seconds}} = \frac{200 \text{ meters}}{s \text{ seconds}}$ $\approx$ **14.55 sec**

8. $\frac{464 \text{ feet}}{8 \text{ days}} = \frac{522 \text{ feet}}{d \text{ days}}$ **9 days**

9. $\frac{\$178.50}{17 \text{ hours}} = \frac{\$ d}{28 \text{ hours}}$ **$294**

10. Jonathan conducted 24 telephone surveys in 6 hours. At this rate, how long will it take him to conduct 15 more telephone surveys? **3.75 h**

Ratios, Proportions, and Similarity
SECTION 4A Section A Enrichment: Acceleration

Velocity is a ratio of distance to time. Acceleration is a ratio of change in velocity to time. If a car accelerates from 50 miles/hour to 60 miles/hour in 5 seconds, the acceleration is 2 miles per hour per second.

These three equations can be used to solve problems involving acceleration:

(a) $d = v_o t + \frac{1}{2} a t^2$

(b) $v_f = v_o + at$

(c) $v_f^2 - v_o^2 = 2ad$

d	Distance
v_o	Original velocity, the velocity at the beginning of acceleration
v_f	Final velocity, the velocity at the end of acceleration
a	Acceleration that is constant
t	Time, the time during which acceleration occurs

Suppose a car is traveling at 35 miles per hour and accelerates for 15 seconds at a rate of 1 mile per hour per second. How many feet does the car travel in that 15 seconds?

$d = v_o t + \frac{1}{2} a t^2$

$= \left(35 \cdot \frac{5,280}{3,600}\right)(15) + \frac{1}{2}\left(\frac{5,280}{3,600}\right)(15)^2$

$= 770 + 165 = 935$ ft

$v_o = 35$ miles/hour $= 35 \cdot \frac{5,280}{3,600}$ feet/sec

$a = 1$ mile/hour/sec $= 1 \cdot \frac{5,280}{3,600}$ feet/sec$^2 = \frac{5,280}{3,600}$ feet/sec^2

$t = 15$ seconds

The car travels 935 feet.

1. A car is traveling at 45 miles per hour and accelerates for 10 seconds at a rate of 2 miles per hour per second. About how many feet does the car travel in that 10 seconds? $\approx$ **806.7 feet**

2. A motorcycle accelerates from 0 to 40 miles/hour in 8 seconds.
   a) What it its approximate rate of acceleration in feet per seconds? *Hint:* Use equation (b). $\approx$ **7.3 feet/sec^2**

   b) How many feet does it travel in that period of time? $\approx$ **234.7 feet**

3. A truck accelerates from 0 to 60 miles/hour with a constant acceleration of 1.5 miles/hour/sec. How many feet does it travel in the time it takes to reach 60 miles/hour. *Hint:* Use equation (c). **1,760 feet**

4. Form three different formulas for acceleration, each one based on one of the equations given above. $a = 2\left(\dfrac{d - v_o t}{t^2}\right)$; $a = \dfrac{v_f - v_o}{t}$; $a = \dfrac{v_f^2 - v_o^2}{2d}$

Ratios, Proportions, and Similarity
LESSON 3 Skills Intervention: Similar Figures

Congruent figures have the same size and the same shape, whereas **similar** figures have the same shape but not always the same size. In similar polygons **corresponding angles** must be congruent and **corresponding sides** must have lengths that form equivalent ratios.

Vocabulary
similar
corresponding sides
corresponding angles

Finding Missing Measures in Similar Figures
A standard 4 inch long by 6 inch wide photo is scaled down to 1.5 inch long to fit in a photo key chain. How wide should the picture be in the key chain for the two pictures to be similar?

What is the known length of the scaled picture? **1.5 in.**

What is the corresponding length of the original picture? **4 in.**

$\frac{1.5}{4} = $ **0.375**   Divide the known length by the corresponding length. This is the **scale factor**.

6 in. × **0.375** = **2.25**   Multiply the width of the original picture by the scale factor.

What is the width of the new picture? **2.25 in.**

Architecture Application
An architect draws a blueprint of a house. He draws the length of the house 15 inches and the width 6 inches. If the actual length is 60 feet, what is the width?

What is the length of the house on the blueprint? **15 in.**

What is the width of the house on the blueprint? **6 in.**

What is the length of the actual house? **60 ft**

What is the unknown? **the width of the actual house**

Set up a proportion as shown.

$\frac{\text{blueprint length}}{\text{blueprint width}} = \frac{\text{actual length}}{\text{actual width}}$ $\frac{15 \text{ in.}}{6 \text{ in.}} = \frac{60 \text{ ft}}{x}$

What are the cross products? **15 in.** · x ft = **60 ft** · 6 in.

Are the same units on both sides of the equal sign? **yes** Cancel them.

Multiply each side. **15** x = **360**

Divide to isolate x. $x = $ **24**

What is the width of the actual house? **24 feet**

Ratios, Proportions, and Similarity
LESSON 3 Problem Solving Intervention: Similar Figures

Similar figures have the same shape, but not necessarily the same size. The ratio formed by corresponding sides is the scale factor.

A photo of a candidate for mayor is 6 inches tall and 4.5 inches wide. It is being enlarged to become a campaign poster that will be 2.5 feet tall. How wide will the poster be, if the pictures are similar?

Understand the Problem

1. What is true about the sides and angles of similar figures?
   Sides are proportional, angles are congruent.

2. Identify the corresponding sides of the photo and poster.
   The 6-inch height of the photo corresponds to the 2.5-foot height of the poster. The 4.5-inch width of the photo corresponds to the unknown width of the poster.

Make a Plan

3. Using the ratio of the scale factor on one side of an equation, what can you form with another ratio to help you find the unknown width of the poster?
   a proportion

4. In order to compare equivalent units, what dimension should you use in the equation for the height of the poster? **30 inches**

Solve

5. Form a proportion using x for the unknown width of the poster.
   Possible Answer: $\frac{\text{height of poster}}{\text{height of photo}} = \frac{\text{width of poster}}{\text{width of photo}}$, $\frac{30}{6} = \frac{x}{4.5}$

6. Cross multiply then simplify to isolate x. What will be the width of the poster? **22.5 inches**

Look Back

7. The photo and poster are similar figures, so the ratio of height to width for each should be the same. Show whether this is true.
   $\frac{30}{22.5} = \frac{6}{4.5} = 1.\overline{3}$

© Houghton Mifflin Harcourt Publishing Company

Ratios, Proportions, and Similarity
LESSON 4 Skills Intervention: Dilations

A **dilation** is an enlargement or reduction of a figure without changing its shape. A **scale factor** describes how much a figure is enlarged or reduced. The **center of dilation** is a fixed point that connects each pair of corresponding vertices.

Vocabulary
dilation
center of dilation
scale factor

Identifying Dilations
Tell whether each transformation is a dilation.

A.

B.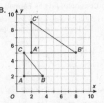

Is the transformation a dilation? _yes_

Is the transformation a dilation? _no_

Using the Origin as the Center of Dilation

Dilate the figure by a scale factor of $\frac{3}{4}$. What are the coordinates of the image?

What do you need to multiply each coordinate by? ___the scale factor, $\frac{3}{4}$___

$\triangle ABC$ $\triangle A'B'C'$

$A(2, 6) \rightarrow A'\left(2 \cdot \frac{3}{4}, 6 \cdot \frac{3}{4}\right) \rightarrow A'$ _(1.5, 4.5)_

$B(4, 6) \rightarrow B'\left(4 \cdot \frac{3}{4}, 6 \cdot \frac{3}{4}\right) \rightarrow B'$ _(3, 4.5)_

$C(4, 8) \rightarrow C'\left(4 \cdot \frac{3}{4}, 8 \cdot \frac{3}{4}\right) \rightarrow C'$ _(3, 6)_

Sketch the dilated figure on the same coordinate plane.

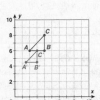

Ratios, Proportions, and Similarity
LESSON 4 Problem Solving Intervention: Dilations

For some problems, you can choose coordinates that will be easy to work with.

A square with an area of 16 cm² is dilated with a scale factor of 2.5. What is the area of the dilated square?

Understand the Problem

1. Will the area of the dilated square be greater than 16 cm²? Explain.

   Yes; since the scale factor > 1, the square is being enlarged.

2. By what number would you multiply the coordinates of a vertex on the square to find its new coordinates after the dilation? ___2.5___

Make a Plan

3. How would it help to draw the original square on a coordinate plane?

   That way you can simply multiply the coordinates of each corner by 2.5 to see the dilated square.

4. Why would it make sense to use (0,0) as one corner?

   The simpler the coordinates, the simpler it will be to multiply them by 2.5.

5. What is the length of the original square? Explain.

   4 cm; The area is 16 cm², so the length must be 4 cm, since 4 cm • 4 cm = 16 cm².

Solve

6. On the grid, draw the original square with the lower left corner at (0, 0). Label the coordinates of each corner of the square.

7. Multiply to find the coordinates of the corners of the dilated square. Draw it and label the coordinates of each corner.

8. What is the area of the dilated square?

   100 cm²

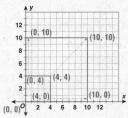

Look Back

9. Make sure your multiplication and your diagram are accurate.

Ratios, Proportions, and Similarity
SECTION 4B SECTION B: Quiz for Lessons 3 Through 4

3 Similar Figures

1. Which rectangles are similar? ___A and C___

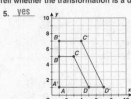

2. Jaime found a picture that he wanted to fit into a collage he was making. The picture was 5 inches wide and 4 inches tall. He enlarged the picture to a width of 12.5 inches. How tall was the enlarged picture? ___10 inches___

3. Laura had a photo of her dog that she wanted to enlarge to fill a frame. The original photo was 5 inches wide and 8 inches tall. The enlargement was 9.6 inches tall. How wide was the enlargement? ___6 inches___

4. A computer screen contained the picture of an office building. The measurement of the building on the screen was 14 cm tall by 2.6 cm wide. The image was projected onto a wall where the height of the building measured 91 cm. What was the width of the building as measured on the wall? ___16.9 cm___

4 Dilations
Tell whether the transformation is a dilation.

5. _yes_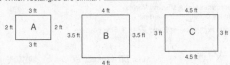

6. _no_

7. A triangle has vertices with coordinates (0,0), (−3, 4), and (5, −1). If the triangle is dilated by a scale factor of 2 with the origin as the center of dilation, what are the coordinates of the vertices of the image?

   (0, 0), (−6, 8), (10, −2)

Ratios, Proportions, and Similarity
SECTION 4B Section B Enrichment: Aspect Ratios

Aspect ratio is the ratio of the width of a picture to the height of a picture. The screens of traditional television sets have an aspect ratio of 4:3, or 1.33:1. One common aspect ratio used for films today is the widescreen format of 1.85:1.

1. The diagram on the right shows what happens when the full height of a movie with an aspect ratio of 1.85:1 is shown on a standard TV screen. About what percent of the original image appears to get cut off?

   About 25%

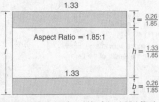
Width of Original Film
TV Screen

The situation gets a little more interesting when the full width of a movie with an aspect ratio of 1.85:1 is shown centered on a standard TV screen.

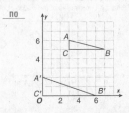

Aspect Ratio = 1.85:1

$t = \frac{0.26}{1.85}$

$h = \frac{1.33}{1.85}$

$b = \frac{0.26}{1.85}$

2. In the diagram, the width of the 1.85:1 film is shown conforming to the width of the 1.33:1 TV screen. Write and solve a proportion to find the relative height h of the displayed film. Fill in that dimension on the diagram, leaving it as a fraction.

   $\frac{1.85}{1} = \frac{1.33}{h}$ $h = \frac{1.33}{1.85}$

3. The unused areas of the TV screen, shown in gray, are equal in size. Use the dimension you found for h to determine relative dimensions for t and b. Fill in those dimensions on the diagram leaving them as fractions.

4. About what percent of the TV screen is used by the film image? How does that compare with your answer to question 1?

   72%; The percent of original film lost when the height of the film is preserved looks about the same as the percent of the TV screen lost when the width of the screen is preserved.

Lesson 1 — Geometric Relationships

Ready to Go On?

LESSON 1 — Geometric Relationships

Skills Intervention: Angle Relationships

An **angle** is made of two rays with a common vertex.

A **right angle** measures 90°, an **obtuse angle** measures greater than 90° but less than 180°, and an **acute angle** measures less than 90°. Two acute **angles** are said to be **complementary** if their measures add to 90° and **supplementary** if their measures add to 180°.

Vocabulary
right angle
obtuse angle
acute angle
angle
complementary angles
supplementary angles
adjacent angles
vertical angles
congruent angles

Use the figure to the right to answer each question.

Classifying Angles

A. Name a right angle in the figure.

How many degrees are in a right angle? $\underline{90°}$

Name a right angle. $\underline{\angle BFD}$

B. Name two obtuse angles in the figure.

An obtuse angle has a measure greater than $\underline{90°}$ but less than $\underline{180°}$.

Name two obtuse angles. $\underline{\angle EBD, \angle ABF}$

Some angles have special relationships. **Adjacent angles** have a common vertex and a common side, but no common interior points. **Vertical angles** are nonadjacent angles made by two intersecting lines. **Congruent angles** have the same measure.

Finding Angle Measures
Use the diagram to find the angle measure.

If $m\angle CBF = 40°$, find $m\angle FBA$.

$m\angle CBF + m\angle FBA = \underline{180°}$ The angles are $\underline{\text{supplementary}}$.

$\underline{40°} + m\angle FBA = \underline{180°}$ Substitute $\underline{40°}$ for $m\angle CBF$.

$\underline{-40°} \qquad \underline{-40°}$ Subtract $\underline{40°}$ from both sides.

$m\angle FBA = \underline{140°}$

60   Holt McDougal Mathematics

Lesson 2 — Geometric Relationships

Ready to Go On?

LESSON 2 — Geometric Relationships

Skills Intervention: Parallel and Perpendicular Lines

Parallel lines are two lines in a plane that never meet and **perpendicular lines** intersect at 90° angles. A line that intersects two or more lines is called a **transversal**. When two parallel lines are intersected by a transversal, the acute angles and obtuse angles that are formed are congruent and any acute angle is supplementary to any obtuse angle.

Vocabulary
parallel lines
perpendicular lines
transversal

Identifying Congruent Angles Formed by a Transversal

Lines m and n are parallel. Use a protractor to measure the angles formed when the transversal intersects the parallel lines. Which angles seem to be congruent?

Find the measure of:

$\angle 1\ \underline{150°}$ $\angle 2\ \underline{30°}$ $\angle 3\ \underline{30°}$ $\angle 4\ \underline{150°}$

$\angle 5\ \underline{150°}$ $\angle 6\ \underline{30°}$ $\angle 7\ \underline{30°}$ $\angle 8\ \underline{150°}$

Which angles are congruent to $\angle 2$? $\underline{\angle 3,}$ $\underline{\angle 6,}$ and $\underline{\angle 7}$

Which angles are congruent to $\angle 1$? $\underline{\angle 4,}$ $\underline{\angle 5,}$ and $\underline{\angle 8}$

Finding Angle Measures of Parallel Lines Cut by Transversals

In the figure, line p ‖ line q. Find the measure of each angle.

A. $\angle 7$

What type of angle is $\angle 7$? $\underline{\text{obtuse}}$

What is the measure of the angle opposite $\angle 7$? $\underline{118°}$

When parallel lines are cut by a transversal, all obtuse angles are $\underline{\text{congruent}}$

So, $m\angle 7 = \underline{118°}$.

B. $\angle 5$

When parallel lines are cut by a transversal, any $\underline{\text{acute}}$ angle formed is supplementary to any $\underline{\text{obtuse}}$ angle formed.

What is the sum of two supplementary angles? $\underline{180°}$

$\angle 5$ is $\underline{\text{supplementary}}$ to 118°.

$m\angle 5 + 118° = \underline{180°}$ Write an equation to find $m\angle 5$.

$\underline{-118°} \quad \underline{-118°}$ Subtract.

$m\angle 5 = \underline{62°}$

61   Holt McDougal Mathematics

Lesson 3 — Geometric Relationships

Ready to Go On?

LESSON 3 — Geometric Relationships

Skills Intervention: Triangles

The **Triangle Sum Theorem** states that the angle measures of any triangle in a plane add up to 180°. Triangles are classified by their angle measures. **Acute triangles** have 3 acute angles. **Right triangles** have 1 right angle. **Obtuse triangles** have 1 obtuse angle. Triangles are also classified by their side lengths. **Equilateral triangles** have 3 congruent sides and 3 congruent angles. **Isosceles triangles** have at least 2 congruent sides and 2 congruent angles. **Scalene triangles** have no congruent sides and no congruent angles.

Vocabulary
Triangle Sum Theorem
acute triangle
right triangle
obtuse triangle
equilateral triangle
isosceles triangle
scalene triangle
Triangle Inequality Theorem

Finding Angles in Acute and Right Triangles

Find x in the acute triangle.

What is the sum of the angles in an acute triangle? $\underline{180°}$

$55° + 75° + x° = \underline{180°}$

$130° + x° = 180°$ Add.

$\underline{-130°} \qquad \underline{-130°}$ What should you subtract from each side to isolate x?

$x° = \underline{50°}$ What is the measure of x?

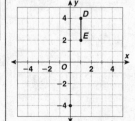

The **Triangle Inequality Theorem** states that the sum of the lengths of any two sides of a triangle is greater than the length of the third side.

Using the Triangle Inequality Theorem
Tell whether a triangle can have sides with the given lengths.
3 ft, 6 ft, 8 ft

Find the sum of the lengths of two sides, and compare it to the third side.

$3 + \underline{6} \overset{?}{>} 8$ $\underline{3} + 8 \overset{?}{>} 6$ $8 + 6 \overset{?}{>} \underline{3}$

$\underline{9} > 8$ $\underline{11} > 6$ $\underline{14} > 3$

Is the sum of the lengths of any two sides greater than the length of the third side? $\underline{\text{yes}}$

Can a triangle have these side lengths? $\underline{\text{yes}}$

62   Holt McDougal Mathematics

Lesson 4 — Geometric Relationships

Ready to Go On?

LESSON 4 — Geometric Relationships

Skills Intervention: Coordinate Geometry

The **midpoint** of a line segment is the point that divides the segment into two congruent segments.

Vocabulary
midpoint

Finding the Coordinates of a Missing Vertex
Find the coordinates of the missing vertex.

Triangle DEF has a right angle at E and $\overline{EF} = 3$. Find possible coordinates for F.

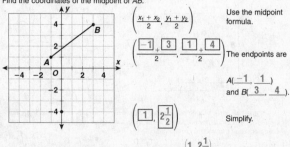

Since $\overline{DE}$ is vertical, $\overline{EF}$ must be $\underline{\text{horizontal}}$ to make a right angle.

Point F could be $\underline{3}$ units to the left of point E, at $(\underline{-2}, \underline{2})$.

Point F could also be $\underline{3}$ units to the right of point E, at $(\underline{4}, \underline{2})$

The possible coordinates for F are $(\underline{-2}, \underline{2})$ and $(\underline{4}, \underline{2})$.

Finding the Coordinates of a Midpoint
Find the coordinates of the midpoint of $\overline{AB}$.

$\left(\dfrac{x_1 + x_2}{2}, \dfrac{y_1 + y_2}{2}\right)$ Use the midpoint formula.

$\left(\dfrac{\underline{-1} + \underline{3}}{2}, \dfrac{\underline{1} + \underline{4}}{2}\right)$ The endpoints are

$A(\underline{-1}, \underline{1})$ and $B(\underline{3}, \underline{4})$.

$\left(\boxed{1}, \boxed{2\tfrac{1}{2}}\right)$ Simplify.

The coordinates for the midpoint of segment AB are $\left(1, 2\tfrac{1}{2}\right)$

63   Holt McDougal Mathematics

© Houghton Mifflin Harcourt Publishing Company

Geometric Relationships

SECTION 5A SECTION A: Quiz for Lessons 1 Through 4

1 Angle Relationships
Refer to the figure.

1. Name two pairs of complementary angles.

   Possible answers: ∠CBA and ∠ABH, ∠CBD and ∠EBF

2. Name three pairs of supplementary angles above line $\overline{AE}$.

   ∠ABG and ∠GBE, ∠ABH and ∠HBE,

   ∠ABF and ∠FBE

3. Name one right angle. **∠HBC**

4. How many rays are in the figure? **7**

5. Name the segments identified on line $\overleftrightarrow{AE}$.

   $\overline{AB}$, $\overline{AE}$, $\overline{BE}$

6. How many points, in addition to those identified, are located on plane ABC?

   an infinite number of points

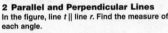

Refer to the figure.

7. Name the right angle. **∠EBD**

8. Name two acute angles. **∠ABE and ∠DBC**

9. Name two obtuse angles. **∠ABD and ∠EBC**

2 Parallel and Perpendicular Lines
In the figure, line $t \parallel$ line r. Find the measure of each angle.

10. ∠1 **70°**   11. ∠2 **110°**

12. ∠3 **70°**   13. ∠4 **110°**

Geometric Relationships

SECTION 5A SECTION A: Quiz for Lessons 1 Through 4, continued

3 Triangles
Find $x°$ in each triangle.

14. **$x° = 49°$**   15. **$x° = 52°$**

Find $x°$ in each triangle.

16. **$x° = 58°$**   17. **$x° = 68°$**

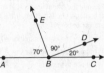

4 Coordinate Geometry
Graph the quadrilaterals with the given vertices. Give all of the names that apply to each quadrilateral.

18. $A(4, 4)$, $B(4, -2)$, $C(-3, -2)$, $D(-2, 4)$

   trapezoid

19. $P(2, 4)$, $Q(2, -1)$, $R(-1, -1)$, $S(-1, 4)$

   rectangle, parallelogram

Name the coordinates of the missing vertex.

20. rectangle $ABCD$ with $A(-3, 2)$, $B(4, 2)$, $C(4, -3)$

   $D(-3, -3)$

21. parallelogram $PQRS$ with $P(-3, 2)$, $Q(-1, 4)$, $R(2, -1)$

   $S(0, -3)$

Geometric Relationships

SECTION 5A Section A Enrichment: Single Point Perspective

Perspective is a technique used to help make a drawing of an object appear the way the actual object appears to the human eye. A main feature of perspective drawing is that some edges that are parallel in an actual object are not drawn as parallel line segments. These non-parallel lines converge at a "vanishing point."

These are the steps for drawing a three-dimensional rectangular solid with single point perspective.

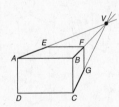

Steps

1. Draw rectangle $ABCD$.

2. Choose any vanishing point V you wish.

3. Draw light lines from each vertex of rectangle $ABCD$ through point V.

4. Choose a point E on line AV. Draw a line from E that is parallel to $\overline{AB}$ and intersects $\overline{BV}$ at F.

5. Draw $\overline{FG}$ parallel to $\overline{BC}$.

6. Darken lines AE, BF, and CG.

You can now apply the same technique to create a three-dimensional drawing of the letter L. Use vanishing point V. You do not have to label any other vertex. When you are finished drawing, shade the two inside surfaces of the figure.

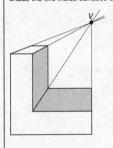

Geometric Relationships

LESSON 5 Skills Intervention: Congruence

Two figures are **congruent figures** if all corresponding sides and angles are congruent. When writing congruence statements between a pair of polygons, the vertices in the second figure are written in order of **correspondence** with the first figure.

Vocabulary
congruent figures
correspondence

Writing Congruence Statements
Write a congruence statement for the pair of polygons.

In polygon #2, which angle is congruent and in the same position as ∠W in polygon #1? **∠M**

In polygon #2, which angle is congruent and in the same position as ∠X in polygon #1? **∠N**

Complete the following statements.

∠Y ≅ ∠K so **∠Y** corresponds to ∠K.

∠Z ≅ **∠L** so ∠Z corresponds to **∠L**.

Complete the statement: trapezoid $WZYX$ ≅ trapezoid **$MLKN$**.

Using Congruence Relationships to Find Unknown Values
pentagon $HIJKL$ ≅ pentagon $TPQRS$

A. Find m.
What angle corresponds to ∠K? **∠R**

What is the measure of these angles? **100°**

$5m = 100$ Write an equation to find m.

$\dfrac{5m}{5} = \dfrac{100}{5}$ Divide to isolate m.

$m =$ **20**   Solve for m.

B. Find n.
What side does $n + 10$ correspond to? **$\overline{SR}$**

$n + 10 = 20$ Write an equation.

$\underline{-10} \quad \underline{-10}$ Undo the addition.

$n =$ **10**   Solve for n.

LESSON 6 — Geometric Relationships
Ready to Go On?
Skills Intervention: Transformations

Three types of **transformations** are:
Translation: slides a figure along a line without turning.
Rotation: turns the figure around a point, called the **center of rotation.**
Reflection: flips the figure across a line to create a mirror **image.**

Vocabulary
transformation
translation
rotation
center of rotation
reflection
image

Graphing Transformations on a Coordinate Plane

If triangle ABC is translated 4 units right, what are the coordinates of the image of point A? __(0, 3)__

Translate triangle ABC 4 units right and label the image $A_1B_1C_1$.

If triangle ABC is rotated 180° clockwise about (0, 0), the rotated image of side BC will be __parallel__ to side BC.

Rotate triangle ABC 180° clockwise about (0, 0) and label the image $A_2B_2C_2$.

If triangle ABC is reflected across the x-axis, what are the coordinates of the image of point C? __(−4, −1)__

Reflect triangle ABC across the x-axis and label the image $A_3B_3C_3$.

Graphing Reflections on a Coordinate Plane
Graph the reflection of quadrilateral $FGHJ$ across the y-axis.

If quadrilateral $FGHJ$ is reflected across the y-axis, will the x-coordinates of the reflection stay the same? __no__

If quadrilateral $FGHJ$ is reflected across the y-axis, will the y-coordinates of the reflection stay the same? __yes__

To find the coordinates of the reflection, multiply the __x__-coordinate of each vertex by __−1__.

$F(2, 4) \rightarrow F'(\underline{−2}, \underline{4})$
$G(3, 2) \rightarrow G'(\underline{−3}, \underline{2})$
$H(3, 1) \rightarrow H'(\underline{−3}, \underline{1})$
$J(1, 2) \rightarrow J'(\underline{−1}, \underline{2})$
Graph $F'G'H'J'$.

LESSON 7 — Geometric Relationships
Ready to Go On?
Skills Intervention: Similarity and Congruence Transformations

Identifying Similarity Transformations
Identify the transformation from the original to the image and tell whether the two figures are similar or congruent?

What are the coordinates of A? __(−4, −2)__
What are the coordinates of A'? __(−2, −1)__
What are the coordinates of B? __(−4, 4)__
What are the coordinates of B'? __(−2, 2)__
What are the coordinates of C? __(4, −2)__
What are the coordinates of C'? __(2, −1)__

What is the length of AB? __6__ What is the length of $A'B'$? __3__
What is the length of AC? __8__ What is the length of $A'C'$? __4__
What is the length of BC? __10__ What is the length of $B'C'$? __5__

Look for a relationship among the coordinates. Look for a relationship among the lengths of the sides.

The transformation is a __dilation__ and the figures are __similar__.

Identifying Congruence Transformations
Identify the transformation from the original to the image and tell whether the two figures are similar or congruent?

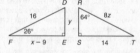

What are the coordinates of A? __(−4, 1)__
What are the coordinates of A'? __(4, 1)__
What are the coordinates of B? __(−4, 4)__
What are the coordinates of B'? __(4, 4)__
What are the coordinates of C? __(0, 1)__
What are the coordinates of C'? __(0, 1)__

What is the length of AB? __3__ What is the length of $A'B'$? __3__
What is the length of AC? __4__ What is the length of $A'C'$? __4__
What is the length of BC? __5__ What is the length of $B'C'$? __5__

Look for a relationship among the coordinates. Look for a relationship among the lengths of the sides.

The transformation is a __reflection__ and the figures are __congruent__.

LESSON 8 — Geometric Relationships
Ready to Go On?
Skills Intervention: Identifying Combined Transformations

Transformation Sequences and Congruence
Identify the combined transformations from the original to the final image and tell whether the two figures are similar or congruent?

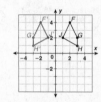

Name the coordinates.	Name the coordinates.	Name the coordinates.
A (−4, 4)	B (−4, 2)	C (−1, 1)
A' (1, 3)	B' (1, 1)	C' (4, 0)
A'' (1, −3)	B'' (1, −1)	C'' (4, 0)

Look for a relationship among the coordinates
The images are __congruent__.

Transformation Sequences and Similarity
Identify the combined transformations from the original to the final image and tell whether the two figures are similar or congruent?

Name the coordinates.	Name the coordinates.	Name the coordinates.
A (−3, −4)	A' (1, −2)	A'' (2, −4)
B (−2, −3)	B' (2, −1)	B'' (4, −2)
C (−2, −1)	C' (2, 1)	C'' (4, 2)
D (−4, −1)	D' (0, 1)	D'' (0, 2)
E (−4, −3)	E' (0, −1)	E'' (0, −2)

Look for a relationship among the coordinates
The original and final images are __similar__.

Finding Sequences of Transformations
Find a sequence of at least two combined transformations from the original to the final image.
What are the coordinates of the vertices of $ABCD$?
(1, −4), (4, −4), (2, −1), (1, −1)
What are the coordinates of the vertices of $A'B'C'D'$?
(−1, 4), (−4, 4), (−2, 1), (−1, 1)
What are the coordinates of the vertices of $A''B''C''D''$?
(1, 4), (4, 4), (2, 1), (1, 1)
The sequence has __congruence__ transformations.

SECTION 5B — Geometric Relationships
Ready to Go On?
SECTION B: Quiz for Lessons 5 Through 8

5 Congruence
In the figure, triangle $DEF \cong$ triangle RST.

1. Find x. __23__
2. Find z. __2__

In the figure, quadrilateral $ABCD \cong$ quadrilateral $EFGH$

3. Find r. __8__
4. Find s. __27__
5. Find t. __4.8__

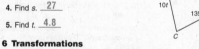

6 Transformations
Identify each as a translation, reflection, rotation, or none of these.

6.

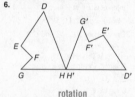

__rotation__

7.

__translation__

Quadrilateral $JKLM$ has vertices $J(0, 0)$, $K(5, 0)$, $L(4, −4)$, $M(0, −6)$. Find the coordinates of the image of each point after each transformation.

8. 90° clockwise rotation about (0,0), point K
__(0, −5)__

9. reflection across the y-axis, point J
__(0, 0)__

10. translation 5 units up, point L
__(4, 1)__

11. 180° clockwise rotation about (0,0), point M
__(0, 6)__

SECTION 5B Geometric Relationships

7 Similarity and Congruence Transformations

Identify each transformation from the original to the image, and tell whether the two figures are similar or congruent.

12. Original: $A(-2, 5)$, $B(3, 5)$, $C(3, -1)$, $D(-2, -1)$

Image: $A'(2, 5)$, $B'(-3, 5)$, $C'(-3, -1)$, $D'(2, -1)$

__reflection across the y-axis; congruent__

13. Original: $A(-4, 8)$, $B(0, 4)$, $C(-4, -8)$, $D(-8, -4)$

Image: $A'(-1, 2)$, $B'(0, 1)$, $C'(-1, -2)$, $D'(-2, -1)$

__dilation; similar__

14. Original: $A(0, 5)$, $B(5, 1)$, $C(1, 2)$

Image: $A'(-2, 2)$, $B'(3, -2)$, $C'(-1, -1)$

__translation 2 units left and 3 units down; congruent__

15. Original: $A(-8, 7)$, $B(-5, 3)$, $C(-2, 4)$, $D(1, 6)$

Image: $A'(-7, -8)$, $B'(-3, -5)$, $C'(-4, -2)$, $D'(-6, 1)$

__rotation 90° counterclockwise around the origin; congruent__

16. Original: $A(-10, 2)$, $B(-3, -6)$, $C(1, 3)$

Image: $A'(-10, -2)$, $B'(-3, 6)$, $C'(1, -3)$

__reflection across the x-axis; congruent__

8 Identifying Combined Transformations

Identify the combined transformations from the original to the final image, and tell whether the two figures are similar or congruent.

17.

__rotation 180° around the origin;__
__reflection across the x-axis;__
__congruent__

18.

__dilation by a factor of $\frac{1}{2}$ with the__
__origin as the center of dilation;__
__reflection across the x-axis; similar__

SECTION 5B Geometric Relationships

Section B Enrichment: Frieze Designs

A frieze is a pattern that repeats in one direction. It consists of repeated copies of a single figure or block. Frieze patterns, also called border patterns, can be found along the upper edge of wallpaper, on pottery, as decorative design on buildings, and elsewhere. An example of a frieze is below.

As you can see, the same triangle is repeated and it has been reflected horizontally. Name the translation used to make the frieze below.   __rotation__

Five basic transformations used for friezes are listed below at the right. Match each transformation with the frieze that incorporates it.

Rotation __B__

Translation __C__

Reflection Across a Horizontal Line __A__

Reflection Across a Vertical Line __E__

Glide Reflection __D__

LESSON 1 — Measurement and Geometry
Skills Intervention: Circles

A **circle** is a set of points in a plane that are a fixed distance from a given point, called the center.

Vocabulary
circle
diameter
radius
circumference

The **circumference** is the distance around a circle, $C = \pi d$ or $C = 2\pi r$. The formula for the area of a circle is $A = \pi r^2$.

Finding the Circumference of a Circle
Find the circumference of each circle both in terms of π and to the nearest tenth of a unit. Use 3.14 for π.

A. circle with radius 6 cm

$C = \underline{2\pi r}$ Write the formula for the circumference of a circle, if you know the radius.

$C = 2\pi(\underline{6})$ What do you substitute for r?

$C = \underline{12}\pi$ cm   Multiply.

Using a calculator 12π is $\approx \underline{37.68}$ cm.

What is 37.68 rounded to the nearest tenth? $\underline{37.7}$

B. circle with diameter 2.5 in.

$C = \underline{\pi d}$ Write the formula for the circumference of a circle, if you know the diameter.

$C = \pi(\underline{2.5})$ Substitute the value for d into the equation.

$C = 2.5\pi$ in.   Multiply.

$\approx \underline{7.9}$ in.   Use a calculator. Round to the nearest tenth.

Finding the Area of a Circle
Find the area of the circle both in terms of π and to the nearest tenth. Use 3.14 for π.

circle with diameter 2.5 in.
$A = \pi r^2$

$r = \dfrac{d}{2} = \dfrac{2.5}{2} = \underline{1.25}$ What is the relationship between the radius and diameter of a circle?

The radius is one-half the diameter.

$A = \pi\left(\underline{1.25}^2\right)$ Substitute the value of r into the formula.

$A = \underline{4.9}$ in^2 What is the area to the nearest tenth?

LESSON 2 — Measurement and Geometry
Skills Intervention: Volume of Prisms and Cylinders

A prism is a three-dimensional figure named for the shape of its base. A cylinder is a geometric solid with two circular bases. The volume of a solid is the number of cubic units needed to fill the figure. Use these formulas to find the volume.

Prism: $V = Bh$ Cylinder: $V = Bh = (\pi r^2)h$

Finding the Volume of Prisms and Cylinders
Find the volume to the nearest tenth of a unit.

A. What shape is the base of the figure? $\underline{\text{rectangle}}$

How do you find the area of a rectangle? $\underline{\text{base times height}}$

$B = 2 \cdot 4 = \underline{8}$ m^2 Find the area of the base.

$V = \underline{Bh}$ What is the formula for the volume of a prism?

$V = 8 \cdot \underline{8}$ Substitute known values into the formula.

$V = \underline{64}$ m^3 What is the volume?

(figure: rectangular prism 4 m, 8 m, 2 m)

B. What shape is the base of the figure? $\underline{\text{circle}}$

How do you find the area of the base? $\underline{A = \pi r^2}$

What is the length of the radius? $\underline{6 \text{ m}}$

$B = \pi(6^2)$ Find the area of the base.

$B = \underline{36}\pi$ m^2

$V = \underline{Bh}$ Write the formula for the volume of a cylinder.

$V = \underline{36}\pi \cdot \underline{12}$ What values do you substitute for B and h?

$V = \underline{432}\,\pi$ Multiply.

$V \approx \underline{1356.5}$ m^3 Multiply.

(figure: cylinder radius 6 m, height 12 m)

C. What shape is the base of the figure? $\underline{\text{triangle}}$

How do you find the area of a triangle? $\underline{A = \frac{1}{2}bh}$

$B = \frac{1}{2} \cdot \underline{6} \cdot \underline{4} = \underline{12}$ ft^2 What is the area of the base?

What is the formula for the volume of a prism? $\underline{V = Bh}$

What values do you substitute for B and h? $\underline{12 \text{ and } 13}$

$V = Bh$ Find the volume of the prism.

$V = \underline{12} \cdot \underline{13}$

$V = \underline{156}$ ft^3

(figure: triangular prism 4 ft, 6 ft, 13 ft)

SECTION 6A — Measurement and Geometry
SECTION A: Quiz for Lessons 1 Through 2

1 Circles
Find the area and circumference of each circle, both in terms of π and to the nearest tenth. Use 3.14 for π.

1. radius = 14 cm

$C = 28\pi$ cm ≈ 87.9 cm

$A = 196\pi$ cm$^2 \approx 615.4$ cm^2

2. diameter = 8 yd

$C = 8\pi$ yd ≈ 25.1 yd

$A = 16\pi$ yd$^2 \approx 50.2$ yd^2

3. Graph a circle with center $(1, 0)$ that passes through $(1, 2)$. Find the area and circumference, both in terms of π (and to the nearest tenth). Use 3.14 for π.

$C = 4\pi \approx 12.6$ units

$A = 4\pi \approx 12.6$ units^2

2 Volume of Prisms and Cylinders
Find the volume of each figure to the nearest tenth. Use 3.14 for π.

4. (cylinder 4 cm, 10 cm)

502.4 cm^3

5. (triangular prism 8.5 in., 7 in., 5 in.)

148.8 in^3

6. (rectangular prism 3 cm, 6.2 cm, 4.5 cm)

83.7 cm^3

7.  (cylinder 12 ft, 20 ft)

$2,260.8$ ft^3

SECTION 6A — Measurement and Geometry
Section A Enrichment: Bicycle Rotations

When you pedal a bicycle, it makes the wheels rotate and the biker moves forward. Common sizes of bicycle wheels are 12", 24", 26", and 29". Older bicycle may have wheels that are 27". These sizes represent the diameter of the wheel.

1. What measurement of a circle is one complete rotation of a wheel?

$\underline{\text{Circumference}}$

2. Complete the table for each size bicycle wheel to find the distance traveled for one complete rotation. Use 3.14 for π and round to the nearest hundredth

Length of Diameter	12"	24"	26"	27"	29"
in inches	37.68	75.36	81.64	84.78	91.06
in feet	3.14	6.28	6.80	7.07	7.59

For Questions 3–8, round to the nearest whole number.

3. If you ride a 26" bike 500 feet, how many rotations will the tires make?

$\underline{74}$

4. If you ride a 29" bike 1,200 feet, how many rotations will the tires make?

$\underline{158}$

5. If you ride a 12" bike 500 feet, how many rotations will the tires make?

$\underline{159}$

6. If you ride a 27" bike 1 mile, how many rotations will the tires make?

$\underline{747}$

7. If you ride a 24" bike 5 miles, how many rotations will the tires make?

$\underline{4,203}$

8. If you ride a 26" bike and wanted to take a trip where you would have one million rotations, how far in miles would you travel?

$\underline{1,288 \text{ miles}}$

LESSON 3 Measurement and Geometry
Skills Intervention: Volume of Pyramids and Cones

A pyramid is named for the shape of its base. A cone has a circular base. The height of a pyramid or cone is the distance from the highest point to the base along a perpendicular line. Use these formulas to calculate volume.

Pyramid: $V = \frac{1}{3}Bh$ Cone: $V = \frac{1}{3}\pi r^2 h$

Finding the Volume of Pyramids and Cones
Find the volume.

A. What type of base does the figure have? __square__

How do you find the area of the base? __length times width__

$B = 6 \cdot 6 = 36 \text{ in}^2$

$V = \frac{1}{3}Bh$ In the volume formula what does the h represent?
__height of the pyramid__

What does the B represent? __area of the base__

$V = \frac{1}{3}(\underline{36 \cdot 9})$ What values do you substitute for B and h?

$V = \underline{108} \text{ in}^3$ What is the volume of the pyramid?

B. What type of figure is shown? __cone__

What shape is the base? __circle__

How do you find the area of the base? __πr^2__

Find the area of the base. $A = \pi \underline{8}^2 = \underline{64}\pi \text{ ft}^2$

12 ft

8 ft (radius)

What is the formula for the volume of a cone? __$V = \frac{1}{3}Bh$__

Substitute for B and h. $V = \frac{1}{3}(\underline{64\pi \cdot 12})$

$V = \underline{256}\pi$ Use 3.14 for π.

$V = \underline{803.84} \text{ ft}^3$ Multiply.

78   Holt McDougal Mathematics

LESSON 4 Measurement and Geometry
Skills Intervention: Spheres

A **sphere** is a set of points in three dimensions that are a fixed distance from a given point.

Vocabulary
sphere
hemisphere
great circle

Volume Formula   Surface Area Formula
$V = \frac{4}{3}\pi r^3$ $S = 4\pi r^2$

Finding the Volume of a Sphere
Find the volume of a sphere with radius 2 ft, both in terms of π and to the nearest tenth of a unit.

What is the formula for the volume of a sphere? $V = \underline{\frac{4}{3}\pi r^3}$

What value will you substitute for r? $V = \frac{4}{3}\pi (\underline{2})^3$

Simplify the power. $V = \frac{4}{3}\pi \underline{8}$

Multiply. $V = \frac{32}{3}\pi$

Use 3.14 for π. $V \approx \underline{33.5} \text{ ft}^3$

The volume of a sphere with a radius of 2 ft is $\underline{33.5 \text{ ft}^3}$.

The surface area of a sphere is 4 times the area of a great circle. A **great circle** is the edge of a **hemisphere.** A hemisphere is one half of a sphere.

Finding Surface Area of a Sphere
Find the surface area of the sphere shown in terms of π and to the nearest tenth of a unit.

6 in.

$S = \underline{4\pi r^2}$ Write the formula for the surface area of a sphere.

$S = 4\pi(\underline{6})^2$ What value should you substitute for r?

$S = 4\pi(\underline{36})$ Simplify the power.

$S = \underline{144}\pi$ Multiply.

$S \approx \underline{452.2} \text{ in}^2$ Use 3.14 for π.

The surface area of a sphere with a radius of 6 in. is $\underline{452.2 \text{ in}^2}$.

79   Holt McDougal Mathematics

SECTION 6B Measurement and Geometry
SECTION B: Quiz for Lessons 3 Through 4

3 Volume of Pyramids and Cones
Find the volume of each figure to the nearest tenth.
Use 3.14 for π.

1. 7 cm, 6 cm, 10 cm
__70 cm³__

2. 6.5 cm, 4.5 cm
__137.8 cm³__

3. 12 in., 14 in., 5.5 in.
__154 in³__

4. 30 cm, 20 cm
__12,560 cm³__

5. 8 cm, 10 cm, 10 cm
__266.7 cm³__

6. 2.7 cm, 1.8 cm
__9.2 cm³__

4 Spheres
Find the surface area and volume of each sphere with the given measurements, both in terms of π and to the nearest tenth. Use 3.14 for π.

7. radius 7 m
$S = 615.4 \text{ m}^2$,
$V = 1{,}436.0 \text{ m}^3$

8. radius 1.5 cm
$S = 28.3 \text{ cm}^2$,
$V = 14.1 \text{ cm}^3$

9. radius 2.2 ft
$S = 60.8 \text{ ft}^2$,
$V = 44.6 \text{ ft}^3$

10. 8 in
$SA = 256\pi \text{ in}^2$,
803.9 in²
$V = 682\frac{2}{3}\pi \text{ in}^3$
2,143.6 in³

11. 3.4 m
$SA = 11.56\pi \text{ m}^2$,
36.3 m²
$V = 20.6 \text{ m}^3$
6 413/700 π m³

12. 9 ft
$SA = 324\pi \text{ ft}^2$,
1,017.4 ft²
$V = 972\pi \text{ ft}^3$
3,052.1 ft³

80   Holt McDougal Mathematics

SECTION 6B Measurement and Geometry
Section B Enrichment: Giant Pyramids

The Pyramid of the Sun is located in the valley of Teotihuacan, 30 miles north of Mexico City, Mexico. It was built in 150 C.E. in what was then a great city. The Great Pyramid in Gizeh, Egypt, was constructed around 2500 B.C.E. It has an estimated weight of 6.5 million tons.

	Pyramid of the Sun	Great Pyramid
Height	233 ft	481 ft
Side of Base	733 ft	756 ft

1. How does the volume of the Great Pyramid compare to that of the Pyramid of the Sun?

$\dfrac{\text{volume of Great Pyramid}}{\text{volume of Pyramid of the Sun}} = \dfrac{756^2 \cdot 481}{733^2 \cdot 233} \approx \underline{2.2}$

__The volume of the Great Pyramid is about 2.2 times the volume of the__
__Pyramid of the Sun.__

2. The bases of both pyramids are squares. Use the information in the table to calculate the slant height of each pyramid. Use a calculator and show your work.

Pyramid of the Sun slant height = $\sqrt{(233)^2 + (0.5 \cdot 733)^2} \approx$ __434 ft__

Great Pyramid slant height = $\sqrt{(481)^2 + (0.5 \cdot 756)^2} \approx$ __618 ft__

3. If s is the side of a square pyramid and l is the slant height of each side, use the area formulas for a square and a triangle to show that the surface area of the pyramid, including the base, is $s(2l + s)$.

__surface area = area of sides + area of base__

$= 4\left(\frac{1}{2} \cdot [s \cdot l]\right) + s^2$

$= 2sl + s^2$

$= s(2l + s)$

4. How does the surface area of the Great Pyramid compare to that of the Pyramid of the Sun?

$\dfrac{\text{surface area of the Great Pyramid}}{\text{surface area of Pyramid of the Sun}} = \dfrac{756(2 \cdot 618 + 756)}{733(2 \cdot 434 + 733)} \approx \underline{1.28}$

__The surface area of the Great Pyramid is about 1.3 times the surface area__
__of the Pyramid of the Sun.__

81   Holt McDougal Mathematics

LESSON 1 Multi-Step Equations
Skills Intervention: Simplifying Algebraic Expressions

If **terms** have the same variable to the same power, then they are **like terms**. Combining like terms **simplifies** an expression. **Equivalent expressions** have the same value for all values of the variables.

Combining Like Terms to Simplify
Combine like terms. $9n + 8 - 5n + 10$

$9n + 8 - 5n + 10$ — Identify like terms. **9n and 5n, 8 and 10**

$9n - \underline{5n} + 8 + \underline{10}$ — Rewrite and combine coefficients of the like terms.

$\underline{4}\,n + \underline{18}$ — What is the coefficient of n? What is the constant?

Combining Like Terms in Two-Variable Expressions
Combine like terms.

$7m + 3n^2 - m + 8n^2 - 6$

$(7m) + \boxed{3n^2} - (m) + \boxed{8n^2} - 6$ — Identify like terms. Circle terms with an m-variable. Draw a square around terms with an n^2-variable.

$7m - \underline{1}\,m + 3n^2 + 8n^2 - 6$ — Rewrite with like terms together. What is the coefficient on the term m?

$\underline{6}\,m + \underline{11}\,n^2 - 6$ — Combine the coefficients of like terms.

Using the Distributive Property to Simplify
Simplify. $3(6x + 5) - 4x + 12$

$3(6x + 5) - 4x + 12$ — Simplify the parentheses using the **distributive** property.

$3 \bullet \underline{6x} + 3 \bullet \underline{5} - 4x + 12$

$\underline{18x} + \underline{15} - 4x + 12$ — Multiply.

$\underline{18x} - 4x + \underline{15} + 12$ — Rewrite with like terms together.

$\underline{14}\,x + \underline{27}$ — Simplify. What is the coefficient of x? What is the constant?

Combining Like Terms to Solve Algebraic Equations
Solve. $7x + 2x = 81$

$(7x) + (2x) = 81$ — Circle like terms.

$\underline{9x} = 81$ — Add coefficients.

$\frac{9x}{9} = \frac{81}{9}$ — Divide both sides by $\underline{9}$.

$x = \underline{9}$

LESSON 2 Multi-Step Equations
Skills Intervention: Solving Multi-Step Equations

You solve an equation by isolating the variable. To isolate the variable you may have to combine like terms.

Solving Equations that Contain Like Terms
Solve.
$4x + 12 + 8x - 24 = 36$

$(4x) + 12 + (8x) - 24 = 36$ — Circle the terms that contain a variable.

$12x - 12 = 36$ — Combine like terms.

$\underline{+12} \quad \underline{+12}$ — Add $\underline{12}$ to each side to isolate x.

$12x = \underline{48}$

$\frac{12x}{12} = \frac{48}{12}$ — **Divide** each side by 12.

$x = \underline{4}$ — Simplify.

Check:
$4x + 12 + 8x - 24 = 36$

$4(\underline{4}) + 12 + 8(\underline{4}) - 24 \stackrel{?}{=} 36$ — What do you substitute for x? $\underline{4}$

$\underline{16} + 12 + \underline{32} - 24 \stackrel{?}{=} 36$ — Simplify.

$\underline{36} = 36$ ✓

Solving Equations that Contain Fractions
Solve.

$$\frac{5y}{8} + \frac{7}{8} = \frac{-3}{8}$$

$\underline{8} \bullet \left(\frac{5y}{8} + \frac{7}{8}\right) = \underline{8} \bullet \left(\frac{-3}{8}\right)$ — Clear the denominators by multiplying both sides by $\underline{8}$.

$\underline{8}\left(\frac{5y}{8}\right) + \underline{8}\left(\frac{7}{8}\right) = \underline{8}\left(\frac{-3}{8}\right)$ — Use the Distributive Property.

$\underline{5y} + 7 = \underline{-3}$ — Simplify.

$\underline{-7} \quad \underline{-7}$ — Undo the addition.

$5y = \underline{-10}$

$\frac{5y}{5} = \frac{-10}{5}$ — How do you isolate y? **Divide both sides by 5.**

$y = \underline{-2}$ — Solve for y.

LESSON 2 Multi-Step Equations
Problem Solving Intervention: Solving Multi-Step Equations

A baseball player had 243 hits. He singled 21% of the times he batted. He doubled 6% of the times and he tripled 1.5% of the times. He also hit 37 home runs. About how many times did he bat?

Understand the Problem

1. Why don't the percents add up to 100%?

 Sample response: They don't include the home runs, or other things
 that happened when he batted, like walks and outs.

2. What is the sum of the player's singles, doubles, triples, and home runs?

 _243_

Make a Plan

3. Let n be the number of times the player batted. What expression with n describes the number of times he singled? Doubled? Tripled?

 _$0.21n$, $0.06n$, $0.015n$_

4. Write an equation with n to show how the different types of hits add up to 243.

 _$0.21n + 0.06n + 0.015n + 37 = 243$_

Solve

5. Solve the equation you wrote in Exercise 4.
 $0.285n + 37 = 243$, $0.285n = 206$, $n = \frac{206}{0.285}$, $n = $ about 722.8

6. About how many times did the player bat?

 Sample answers: about 723 times, about 720 times, about 725 times

Look Back

7. Substitute your answer for n into the equation you solved to see if the answer checks.

 Sample check: $0.21(723) + 0.06(723) + 0.015(723) + 37 = 243$
 $152 + 43 + 11 + 37 = 243$
 $243 = 243$

LESSON 3 Multi-Step Equations
Skills Intervention: Solving Equations with Variables on Both Sides

When solving multi-step equations, combine like terms or clear fractions before isolating the variable. A **literal equation** is an equation with two or more variables.

Solving Equations with Variables on Both Sides
Solve.
A. $5a + 6 = 6a$

$\underline{-5a} \quad \underline{-5a}$ — To get the variable on the same side of the equation, subtract $\underline{5a}$ from each side.

$6 = a$

B. $7x - 9 = 6 + 2x$ — What is the first step? **Get the variable on one side.**

$\underline{-2x} \quad \underline{-2x}$ — Subtract $2x$ from both sides.

$\underline{5}\,x - 9 = 6$ — Combine like terms.

$\underline{+9} \quad \underline{+9}$ — Undo the -9.

$5x = \underline{15}$ — Add.

$\frac{5x}{5} = \frac{15}{5}$ — Isolate x.

$x = \underline{3}$ — What does x equal?

C. $2a - 6 = 2a + 8$ — How do you get $2a$ to one side?

$\underline{-2a} \quad \underline{-2a}$ — Subtract $2a$ from both sides.

$-6 = 8$ — Is this a true statement? **no**

There is no solution to the equation since there is no number that when substituted for the variable a, would make the equation true.

Solving Multistep Equations with Variables on Both Sides
Solve. $x + 9 + 6x = 2 + x + 1$

$7x + 9 = x + 3$ — What is the first step? **Combine like terms.**

$\underline{-x} \quad \underline{-x}$ — Get x to one side of the equation.

$\underline{6}\,x + 9 = \underline{3}$ — Subtract.

$\underline{-9} \quad \underline{-9}$ — What is the next step? **Subtract 9 from each side.**

$6x = \underline{-6}$

$\frac{6x}{6} = \frac{-6}{6}$ — How do you isolate x? **Divide both sides by 6.**

$x = \underline{-1}$ — Solve for x.

LESSON 3 — Multi-Step Equations
Problem Solving Intervention: Solving Equations with Variables on Both Sides

Jiffy Gym offers two plans. With Plan A, you pay a one-time membership fee of $145 and then $39 every month. With Plan B, you pay no membership fee but you pay $54 every month. After how many months does Plan A become a better deal?

Understand the Problem

1. With Plan A, how often do you pay the $145 membership fee?

   once

2. With Plan A, how much do you pay for 1 month? 2 months?

   $184; $223

3. With Plan B, how much do you pay for 1 month? 2 months?

   $54; $108

Make a Plan

4. With n as the number of months, write expressions for the cost of both plans.

   Plan A: $145 + 39n$, Plan B: $54n$

5. Set the two expressions from Exercise 4 equal to each other. How would solving this equation for n help you solve the problem?

   $145 + 39n = 54n$; It tells the point at which both plans are equal.

Solve

6. Solve the equation you wrote in Exercise 5.

   $145 = 15n$, $n = \frac{145}{15}$, $n = 9\frac{2}{3}$

7. Why should the answer be a whole number of months?

   Sample response: You pay a whole month at a time.

8. After how many months does Plan A become a better deal?

   after 9 months

Look Back

9. Complete the table to check your answer.

   $n - 1$
   n
   $n + 1$

months	Plan A	Plan B
9	$496	$486
10	$535	$540
11	$574	$594

LESSON 4 — Multi-Step Equations
Skills Intervention: Systems of Equations

A **system of equations** is a set of two or more equations. The **solution of a system** is a set of values that satisfy both equations.

Vocabulary
system of equations
solution of a system of equations

Solving Systems of Equations
Solve the system of equations.

$y = -x + 6$
$y = x - 2$ What are both equations equal to? y
$-x + 6 = x - 2$ Set the equations equal to each other.
$\underline{+x \quad +x}$ Get x on one side of the equation.
$\underline{6} = \underline{2}x - 2$ Combine like terms.
$\underline{8} = 2x$ Get the constant terms to one side of the equation.
$\frac{8}{2} = \frac{2x}{2}$ How do you isolate x? Divide by 2.
$\underline{4} = x$ Solve for x.
$y = x - 2$ Choose one of the original equations to solve for y.
$y = \underline{4} - 2$ To find y, substitute 4 for x into the original equation.
$y = \underline{2}$

The solution to the system is (4 , 2).

Solving Systems of Equations by Solving for a Variable

$2x - y = 4$
$6x + 3y = 12$

Solve each equation for y.

$2x - y = 4$ $6x + 3y = 12$
$\underline{-y} = -2x + 4$ $3y = \underline{-6x} + 12$
$y = \underline{2x - 4}$ $y = \underline{-2x} + 4$

$\underline{-2x} + 4 = 2x - \underline{4}$ Set the equations equal to each other.
$4 = \underline{4}x - 4$ Get x to one side of the equation.
$8 = 4x$ Add 4 to both sides.
$\frac{8}{4} = \frac{4x}{4}$ Divide both sides by 4.
$\underline{2} = x$ Solve for x.

Substitute x into either original equation: $y = 2x - 4 = 2(2) - 4 = \underline{0}$
The solution set is (2 , 0).

LESSON 4 — Multi-Step Equations
Problem Solving Intervention: Systems of Equations

Even if a system of equations contains 3 variables, you may be able to find out something about the variables.

In this system of equations, there is only one value that x can have. What is it?

$x + y + z = 100$
$x - y - z = 60$

Understand the Problem

1. Complete and the explain why x cannot equal 30.

   $(30) + y + z = 100$ $y + z = \underline{70}$
   $(30) - y - z = 60$ $y + z = \underline{-30}$

   y and z cannot have 2 different sums.

Make a Plan

2. Rewrite each equation by solving for y.

   $x + y + z = 100$ $y = \underline{100} - \underline{x} - \underline{z}$
   $x - y - z = 60$ $y = x - \underline{60} - \underline{z}$

3. Write an equation to show that the two expressions you wrote in Exercise 2 are equal.

   $100 - x - z = x - 60 - z$

Solve

4. Solve the equation you wrote in Exercise 3.

   $100 - x - z = x - 60 - z$
   $\underline{+ x + z \quad + x \quad + z,}$
   $100 = 2x - 60,$
   $160 = 2x$
   $x = 80$

Look Back

5. Substitute your answer for x into the two equations and simplify. Can both equations be true?

   $(\underline{80}) + y + z = 100$ $y + z = \underline{20}$,
   $(\underline{80}) - y - z = 60$ $y + z = \underline{20}$

   Yes, with $x = 80$ both equations will be true if y and z have a sum of 20.

SECTION 7A — Multi-Step Equations
SECTION A: Quiz for Lessons 1 Through 4

1 Simplifying Algebraic Expressions
Simplify.

1. $2x + 7x$

   $9x$

2. $6y - 5y$

   y

3. $3p + 8q + 6p - q$

   $9p + 7q$

4. $3(f + 2) + f$

   $4f + 6$

5. $6s - 3t + 9$

   $6s - 3t + 9$

6. $5(2g - 1) - 4g$

   $6g - 5$

Solve.

7. $3m + 2m = 15$

   $m = 3$

8. $10p - 7p = 18$

   $p = 6$

9. $-12z + 13z = 17$

   $z = 17$

10. $11x - x = 90$

    $x = 9$

11. $44b - 33b + 4b = 60$

    $b = 4$

12. $20s + 30s + 10s = 120$

    $s = 2$

2 Solving Multi-Step Equations
Solve.

13. $5y + 4y - 11 = 16$

    $y = 3$

14. $\frac{7x}{9} - \frac{2x}{9} = \frac{10}{9}$

    $x = 2$

15. $\frac{r}{3} - \frac{r}{5} = \frac{4}{15}$

    $r = 2$

16. $\frac{3b}{8} + \frac{b}{4} = \frac{5}{2}$

    $b = 4$

17. $\frac{1}{5}s + \frac{2}{3}s = 6$

    $s = \frac{90}{13}$ or $6\frac{12}{13}$

18. $\frac{2}{3}t + 1 + \frac{1}{4}t = -5$

    $t = -\frac{72}{11}$ or $-6\frac{6}{11}$

Multi-Step Equations
SECTION 7A | SECTION A: Quiz for Lessons 1 Through 4, continued

3 Solving Equations with Variables on Both Sides

19. $3a + 13 = 5a + 5$

  $a = 4$

20. $8b + 14 = 4b + 38$

  $b = 6$

21. $-3w + 4 + w = 4w + 28$

  $w = -4$

22. $\frac{5}{6}x - \frac{1}{3} = x - \frac{3}{2}$

  $x = 7$

23. $3x + 9y = 6m$

  $x = 2m - 3y$

24. $\frac{14x + y}{d} = 7$

  $x = \frac{1}{2}d - \frac{1}{14}y$

25. The pentagon and the triangle have the same perimeter. What is the measure of this perimeter?

  16

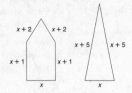

4 Systems of Equations
Solve each system of equations.

26. $y = 2x + 5$
  $y = 3x + 3$
  $(2, 9)$

27. $y = 6x - 8$
  $y = 2x + 4$
  $(3, 10)$

28. $y = 2x - 1$
  $y = -2x + 3$
  $(1, 1)$

29. $x + 3y = -4$
  $-x + y = 0$
  $(-1, -1)$

30. $3x + y = 10$
  $2x - y = -10$
  $(0, 10)$

31. $3x + y = 15$
  $x = -2y + 10$
  $(4, 3)$

32. The sum of two winter temperatures is -10 degrees. Their difference is 34 degrees. Write a system of equations to describe the sum and the difference. Solve this system to find the two temperatures.

  $x + y = -10,\ x - y = 34;\ 12°\ \text{and}\ -22°$

Multi-Step Equations
SECTION 7A | Section A Enrichment: Of Hippos and Chairs

Begin at **START**. Solve the equation in the box. Find the solution (in parentheses) in another box. Draw a line with an arrow from the box with the equation to the box with its solution. Now solve the equation in the second box and find its solution in a third box. Remember to draw a line with an arrow. Continue this way until you reach **FINISH**.

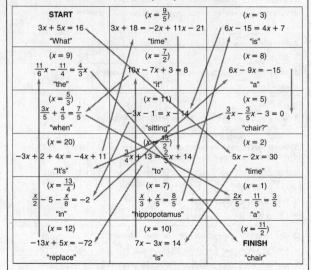

Each box on your path has a word in quotation marks in it. Write these words below in the exact order in which you came upon them.

What time is it when a hippopotamus is sitting in a chair? It's time to replace the chair.

LESSON 1 — Graphing Lines
Skills Intervention: Graphing Linear Equations

A **linear equation** is an equation whose solutions fall on a line on the coordinate plane. If the equation is linear, a constant change in the x-value corresponds to a constant change in the y-value.

Vocabulary
linear equation
rate of change

Graphing Equations
Graph each equation and tell whether it is linear.

A. $y = 3x - 2$
Create a table of values.

x	$3x - 2$	y	(x, y)
-2	$3(-2) - 2$	-8	$(-2, -8)$
-1	$3(\underline{-1}) - 2$	-5	$(-1, \underline{-5})$
0	$3(\underline{0}) - 2$	-2	$(0, \underline{-2})$
1	$3(\underline{1}) - 2$	1	$(1, 1)$
2	$3(\underline{2}) - 2$	4	$(2, 4)$

Plot each coordinate pair from the table on the coordinate grid.

Does the equation form a straight line? __yes__

What is the change between each y-value? __+3__

Is the change the same between every y-value? __yes__

The equation $y = 3x - 2$ is a __linear__ equation.

B. $y = x^2 + 1$
Create a table of values.

x	$x^2 + 1$	y	(x, y)
-2	$(-2)^2 + 1$	5	$(-2, 5)$
-1	$(-1)^2 + 1$	2	$(-1, \underline{2})$
0	$(0)^2 + 1$	1	$(0, \underline{1})$
1	$(1)^2 + 1$	2	$(1, 2)$
2	$(2)^2 + 1$	5	$(2, 5)$

Plot each coordinate pair from the table on the coordinate grid.

Does the equation form a straight line? __no__

Is the change between the y-values constant? __no__

The equation $y = x^2 + 1$ is __not__ a linear equation.

LESSON 1 — Graphing Lines
Problem Solving Intervention: Graphing Linear Equations

You can use a graph to check your solution to a linear equation.

Sara's hair grows an average of 0.4 inches per month. She just cut it to a length of 14 inches on August 1. How long will her hair be at the beginning of February if she doesn't cut it again?

Understand the Problem

1. What do you know and what you need to find?

   __length = 14 in. on 8/1; growth rate = 0.4 in./month; find length on 2/1__

Make a Plan

2. Let n be the number of months since August 1. Write an expression with n for the number of inches Sara's hair grows. __0.4n__

3. Fill in the blanks to write an equation that shows how Sara's hair length, ℓ, depends on the number of months since August.

   Length of hair = original length + amount grown

   ℓ = $\underline{14}$ + $\underline{0.4n}$

Solve

4. To find the length of Sara's hair at the beginning of February, what value of n should you use? Explain.

   __n = 6; February 1 is 6 months after August 1.__

5. Use the equation you wrote in Exercise 3 to solve the problem.

   __$\ell = 14 + 0.4n$; $\ell = 14 + 0.4(6)$; $\ell = 14 + 2.4$, $\ell = 16.4$__

6. How long will Sara's hair be at the beginning of February?

   __16.4 in. (or about $16\frac{1}{2}$ in.)__

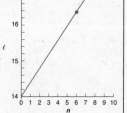

Look Back

7. Check your answer by making a graph and finding the value of ℓ when $n = 6$.

LESSON 2 — Graphing Lines
Skills Intervention: Slope of a Line

Linear equations have a constant slope. The formula for determining

the slope between any two points is $m = \frac{y_2 - y_1}{x_2 - x_1}$.

Vocabulary
rise
run
slope

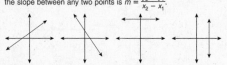

Positive slope   Negative slope   Zero slope   Undefined slope

The **rise** of a line is the difference between the y-values of two points on it. The **run** of a line is the difference in the x-values of two points on it. **Slope** is the ratio of rise to run for any two points on a line.

Finding the Slope of a Line
Find the slope of the line.

The graph is a __straight line__.

The slope is __$\frac{2}{3}$__.

Finding Slope, Given Two Points
Find the slope of the line that passes through $(2, 4)$ and $(8, 2)$.

Let $x_1 = 2$, $y_1 = \underline{4}$, $x_2 = \underline{8}$ and $y_2 = 2$.

$m = \frac{2 - 4}{8 - 2} = \frac{-2}{6} = \frac{-1}{3}$ Substitute the values into the slope formula.

The slope of the line that passes through $(2, 4)$ and $(8, 2)$ is __$-\frac{1}{3}$__.

If the graph of an equation is a straight line, the graph shows a constant rate of change. This means that the slope between any two points on the line is the same. If a graph is not a straight line, it shows a variable rate of change. The slope of the graph changes, depending upon the points used to find the slope.

LESSON 2 — Graphing Lines
Problem Solving Intervention: Slope of a Line

The points in the table are all on a line. Without graphing, find the slope of the line and tell whether it has a constant or a variable rate of change.

x	1	3	5	7
y	4	8	12	16

Understand the Problem

1. What do you know and what are you asked to find?

   __points on a line; the slope of the line and its rate of change__

Make a Plan

2. How can you find the slope of a line without graphing it?

   __find the vertical change over the horizontal change__

3. How can you tell the rate of change without graphing the line?

   __check to see if the slope is the same between any two points__

4. What is the formula for slope? __$\frac{y_2 - y_1}{x_2 - x_1}$__

Solve

5. Use the formula from Exercise 4 to find the slope between $(1, 4)$ and $(3, 8)$.   __$\frac{8 - 4}{3 - 1} = \frac{4}{2} = 2$__

6. Use the formula from Exercise 4 to find the slope between $(5, 12)$ and $(7, 16)$.   __$\frac{16 - 12}{7 - 5} = \frac{4}{2} = 2$__

7. Are the slopes the same? __yes__

8. Answer the question in the problem.

   __The slope of the line is 2. It has a constant rate of change.__

Look Back

9. The equation for the line is $y = mx + 2$. Substitute the slope you found for m and any point on the line for x and y to see if your answer checks.

   __Sample answer: $8 = 2(3) + 2$; $8 = 8$; My answer checks.__

Page 96

The **x-intercept** is where the graph crosses the x-axis and the **y-intercept** is where the graph crosses the y-axis.

Vocabulary
x-intercept
y-intercept
slope-intercept form

Finding x-intercepts and y-intercepts to Graph Linear Equations
Find the x-intercept and y-intercept of the line $4x + 5y = 20$. Use the intercepts to graph the equation.

Find the x-intercept. ($y = 0$)
$4x + 5y = 20$

$4x + 5(\underline{0}) = 20$ Substitute 0 in for y.

$\underline{4}\,x = 20$

$\dfrac{4x}{4} = \dfrac{20}{4}$ What do you divide each side by?

$x = \underline{5}$ Solve for x. The x-intercept is $\underline{5}$.

Find the y-intercept. ($x = 0$)
$4x + 5y = 20$

$4(\underline{0}) + 5y = 20$ Substitute 0 in for x.

$\underline{5}\,y = 20$

$\dfrac{5y}{5} = \dfrac{20}{5}$ What do you divide each side by?

$y = \underline{4}$ Solve for y. The y-intercept is $\underline{4}$.

To graph the equation plot the points $(\underline{5}, 0)$ and $(0, \underline{4})$.

For an equation written in **slope-intercept form**, $y = mx + b$, m is the slope and b is the y-intercept.

Using Slope-Intercept Form to Find Slopes and y-intercepts
Write the equation $3y = 8x$ in slope-intercept form and then find the slope and y-intercept.

What is the slope-intercept form of an equation? $y = \underline{mx + b}$
$3y = 8x$

$\dfrac{3y}{3} = \dfrac{8x}{3}$ By what number do you divide both sides?

$y = \dfrac{8}{3}\,x$ What is the slope? $\underline{\dfrac{8}{3}}$ What is the y-intercept? $\underline{0}$.

Page 97

You can use geometric relationships to find distances on a coordinate plane.

The graph of the equation $y = \frac{3}{4}x + 3$ has an x-intercept and a y-intercept. What is the distance between the two intercepts?

Understand the Problem

1. In what form is the equation $y = \frac{3}{4}x + 3$?

   <u>slope-intercept form</u>

2. In the equation $y = \frac{3}{4}x + 3$, what does the number $\frac{3}{4}$ tell you? What does the number 3 tell you?

   <u>the slope of the line; the y-intercept</u>

3. What is the x-intercept of $y = \frac{3}{4}x + 3$? Graph the equation. Label the x-intercept A and the y-intercept B.

   <u>x-intercept is −4</u>

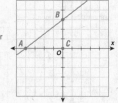

Make a Plan

4. $\overline{AB}$ is a side of $\triangle ABC$. What kind of triangle is $\triangle ABC$?   <u>right triangle</u>

5. If you know the lengths of the two legs of a right triangle, how can you calculate the length of the third side?

   <u>Use the Pythagorean Theorem. $c = \sqrt{a^2 + b^2}$</u>

6. What are the lengths of the two legs of $\triangle ABC$?   <u>3 and 4</u>

Solve

7. Use the Pythagorean Theorem to find AB.

   $AB = \sqrt{3^2 + 4^2} = \sqrt{25} = 5$

   Students may recognize the Pythagorean triplet 3, 4, 5.

Look Back

8. Make sure you graphed the equation correctly. Also, look at $\overline{AB}$ to see if it seems to be about the length you calculated.

Page 98

The **point-slope form** of a linear equation is $y - y_1 = m(x - x_1)$, where m is the slope and (x_1, y_1) is a point on the line.

Vocabulary
point-slope form

Using Point-Slope Form to Identify Information About a Line
Identify a point the line passes through and the slope of the line, given the point-slope form of the equation.

A. $y - 6 = \frac{3}{4}(x - 12)$

   $y - \underline{y_1} = \underline{m}\,(x - \underline{x_1})$ Write the point-slope form of an equation.

   What is m? $\underline{\frac{3}{4}}$ What is x_1? $\underline{12}$ What is y_1? $\underline{6}$

   The line has slope $\frac{3}{4}$ and passes through the point $(\underline{12, 6})$.

B. $y - 4 = 5(x + 8)$

   $y - \underline{y_1} = \underline{m}\,(x - \underline{x_1})$ Write the point-slope form of an equation.

   $y - 4 = 5(x - (\underline{-8}))$ Rewrite using subtraction instead of addition.

   What is m? $\underline{5}$ What is x_1? $\underline{-8}$ What is y_1? $\underline{4}$

   The line has slope $\underline{5}$ and passes through the point $(\underline{-8, 4})$.

Writing the Point-Slope Form of an Equation
Write the point-slope form of the equation with the given slope that passes through the indicated point.

A. the line with slope −3 passing through (5, 2)

Write the point-slope form. $y - \underline{y_1} = \underline{m}\,(x - \underline{x_1})$

Substitute in known values. $y - \underline{2} = \underline{-3}(x - \underline{5})$

B. the line with slope 8 passing through (−2, 6)

Write the point-slope form. $\underline{y} - \underline{y_1} = \underline{m}\,(\underline{x} - \underline{x_1})$

Substitute in known values. $y - \underline{6} = \underline{8}(x - (\underline{-2}))$

Rewrite the equation. $y - \underline{6} = \underline{8}(x + \underline{2})$

Page 99

1 Graphing Linear Equations
Graph each equation and tell whether it is linear.

1. $y = -3 + 2x$ 2. $y = \frac{1}{2}x^2$ 3. $x = y + 4$

<u>linear</u>   <u>not linear</u>   <u>linear</u>

4. A bookstore buys back school books according to the formula $y = \frac{1}{2}x - 5$, where x is the price you originally paid for a book and y is the amount the store will now pay you for it. What is the buy-back price for each of the books listed in the table?

Original Price	Buy-Back Price
$40	<u>$15</u>
$50	<u>$20</u>
$70	<u>$30</u>
$100	<u>$45</u>

2 Slope of a Line
Find the slope of the line that passes through each pair of points.

5. (0, 1) and (4, 3)   6. (−2, 6) and (1, 3)   7. (1, −9) and (3, 1)

   $\underline{\frac{1}{2}}$ $\underline{-1}$ $\underline{5}$

8. (4, 0) and (1, −6)   9. (5, 1) and (−4, 4)   10. (−4, −1) and (2, −1)

   $\underline{2}$ $\underline{-\frac{1}{3}}$ $\underline{0}$

11. The table shows Sam's progress during an all-day hike. Graph the data, find the slope of the line, and explain what the slope shows.

Time	Distance
3 h	9 km
4 h	12 km
5 h	15 km
7 h	21 km

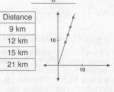

<u>slope = 3; The slope shows that Sam walks at a constant rate of 3 km/h.</u>

Graphing Lines

SECTION 8A SECTION A: Quiz for Lessons 1 Through 4, continued

3 Using Slopes and Intercepts

12. An amusement park charges $20 to get in plus $2 for each ride. The equation $y = 2x + 20$ represents the total amount paid if a person goes on x rides. Identify the slope and the y-intercept and then use them to graph the equation.

slope = 2; y-intercept = 20

Write the equation of the line that passes through each pair of points. Use the slope-intercept form.

13. $(-2, -2)$ and $(4, 1)$

$y = \frac{1}{2}x - 1$

14. $(1, -5)$ and $(-2, 4)$

$y = -3x - 2$

15. $(0, 1)$ and $(-3, 10)$

$y = -3x + 1$

16. $(-5, -3)$ and $(5, -3)$

$y = -3$

17. $(-8, -2)$ and $(4, 1)$

$y = \frac{1}{4}x$

18. $(3, 0)$ and $(1, 1)$

$y = -\frac{1}{2}x + \frac{3}{2}$

4 Point-Slope Form

Use the point-slope form of each equation to identify a point the line passes through and the slope of the line.

19. $y - 1 = 2(x - 2)$

slope = 2

point = (2, 1)

20. $y = -x + 6$

slope = -1

point = (6, 0)

21. $y + 3 = 4x + 2$

slope = 4

point = $(-\frac{1}{2}, -3)$

Write the point-slope form of the equation with the given slope that passes through the indicated point.

22. slope 2, passing through $(1, -1)$

$y + 1 = 2(x - 1)$

23. slope $-\frac{1}{3}$, passing through $(-1, -2)$

$y + 2 = -\frac{1}{3}(x + 1)$

24. slope -4, passing through $(5, 0)$

$y = -4(x - 5)$

25. slope $\frac{2}{3}$, passing through $(-6, 3)$

$y - 3 = \frac{2}{3}(x + 6)$

Graphing Lines

SECTION 8A Section A Enrichment: Clown Face

For each of the following, graph the given point and draw a line with the indicated slope through the point.

1. point: (60, 110)
   slope: 0

2. point: (105, 82)
   slope: -2

3. point: (25, 25)
   slope: -1

4. point: (82, 15)
   slope: $\frac{1}{2}$

5. point: (10, 60)
   slope: undefined

6. point: (38, 105)
   slope: $\frac{1}{2}$

7. point: (105, 38)
   slope: 2

8. point: (38, 15)
   slope: $-\frac{1}{2}$

9. point: (82, 105)
   slope: $-\frac{1}{2}$

10. point: (25, 95)
    slope: 1

11. point: (110, 60)
    slope: undefined

12. point: (15, 82)
    slope: 2

13. point: (95, 95)
    slope: -1

14. point: (60, 10)
    slope: 0

15. point: (15, 38)
    slope: -2

16. point: (95, 25)
    slope: 1

Graphing Lines

LESSON 5 Skills Intervention: Direct Variation

If two variables are related proportionally by a constant ratio, k, then they have a **direct variation**. The ratio is called the **constant of variation**.

$y = kx$ or $k = \frac{y}{x}$

Vocabulary
direct variation
constant of variation

Determining Whether a Data Set Varies Directly
Determine whether the data set shows direct variation.

A.

Stamps	1	2	3	4	5
Price $	0.37	0.74	1.11	1.48	1.85

Make a graph of the data.

Does the line appear to be a straight line? yes

Compare the ratios. $\frac{0.37}{1} = \frac{0.74}{2} = \frac{1.11}{3} = \frac{1.48}{4} = \frac{1.85}{5}$

Reduce each ratio: 0.37, 0.37, 0.37 0.37 0.37

Since the ratios are all the same this is a direct variation

B.

x	3	4	5	6	7
y	8	7.5	6	6.5	5

Make a graph of the data.

Does the line appear to be a straight line? no

Compare the ratios. $\frac{8}{3} = \frac{7.5}{4} = \frac{6}{5} = \frac{6.5}{6} = \frac{5}{7}$

Reduce each ratio: 2.7, 1.9, 1.2 1.1 0.7

Since the ratios are not all the same this is not a direct variation.

Finding Equations of Direct Variation
Find the equation of direct variation, given that y varies directly with x. y is 32 when x is 8.

$y = kx$ Write the direct variation equation.

$32 = k \cdot 8$ Substitute for x and y.

$4 = k$ Substitute 4 back into the original equation.

$y = 4 x$

Graphing Lines

LESSON 5 Problem Solving Intervention: Direct Variation

When you travel at a constant speed, there is a direct variation between distance and time.

A driver sees a log in the road, but it takes time for her to react. During that *reaction time*, the car keeps going at the same speed. The distance the car travels before the driver brakes is the *reaction distance*. At 75 mi/h, the reaction distance is 165 ft. What is the reaction time in seconds?

Understand the Problem

1. Why does it make sense that there is a direct variation between reaction distance and speed?

   Sample answer: If you go twice as fast, you go twice as far in a given amount of time.

2. Suppose the reaction time is 0.5 seconds. What would be the reaction distance at a speed of 100 ft /s?   50 feet

3. How far do you travel during the actual reaction time?   165 feet

Make a Plan

4. How many ft/s is 75 mi/h? Hint: How many times greater is 75 mi/h than 15 mi/h? $15 \frac{mi}{h} = 22 \frac{ft}{s}$

   110 ft/s

5. Let t be the reaction time. Complete the proportion.

   $\frac{165 \text{ feet}}{t \text{ seconds}} = \frac{110 \text{ feet}}{1 \text{ second}}$ ← speed in ft/s

Solve

6. Solve the equation you wrote in Exercise 5.

   $110t = 165$, $t = \frac{165}{110}$, $t = 1.5$

7. How long is the reaction time in seconds?   1.5 seconds

Look Back

8. Start with your answer. See if a car would travel 165 ft in that time if its speed were 75 mi/h.

   1.5 s • 110 ft/s = 165 ft. My answer checks.

LESSON 6 Graphing Lines
Skills Intervention: Solving Systems of Linear Equations by Graphing

When you graph systems of linear equations in the coordinate plane, the solution of the system is where the lines intersect. If the lines don't intersect, the system doesn't have a solution.

Graphing a System of Linear Equations to Solve a Problem

Evan can type 30 words per minute, and Billie can type 60 words per minute. If Evan has already typed 120 words when Billie starts typing, how many minutes will it take Billie to catch up to Evan? How may words will Billie have typed?

Let t = the number of minutes.
Let w = the number of words typed.

If Evan started typing at $t = 0$, an expression for his typing speed is:

$w = 30t + 120$

Which would make the expression for Billie's typing speed:

$w = 60t$

Graph each equation.
The point of intersection is __(4, 240)__.

It has taken Billie __4__ minutes to catch up with Evan. In that time she has typed __240__ words.

Solving Systems of Linear Equations by Graphing

Solve each linear system by graphing. Check your answer.

$x + y = 3$
$y - 2x = -3$

$y = $ __3 − x__ and $y = $ __2x − 3__

Graph the two equations.
The point of intersection is __(2, 1)__.

Check by setting $y = y$.

$3 - x$ = $2x - 3$
3 = $3x - 3$
6 = $3x$
2 = x ✓

LESSON 6 Graphing Lines
Problem Solving Intervention: Solving Systems of Linear Equations by Graphing

Graphing systems of equations can help you solve word problems. It takes Brenton 8 days to crochet two blankets. Holly can crochet 2 blankets in 4 days. If Holly starts crocheting when Brenton completes his first blanket, how long will it be before she has crocheted as much as he has?

Understand the Problem

1. Is the answer to the question a point of intersection? Explain.

   No. The answer to the problem is the number of days it takes Holly
   to catch up to Brenton. It is the x-value of the point of intersection.

Make a Plan

2. When writing your equations and graphing them, will you have Holly or Brenton begin crocheting at (0, 0)? Explain.

   Possible answer: Holly, because it's easiest to write and graph an
   equation where she starts at 0.

3. At what point will you have the other person when $t = 0$?

   I'll have Brenton at (0, 1) because he'll have completed one blanket

Solve

4. Write an equation for Brenton's progress, and one for Holly's progress.

   $y = \frac{1}{4}t + 1$

   $y = \frac{1}{2}t$

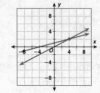

5. Graph the equations and determine the point of intersection. __(4, 2)__

6. When did Holly catch up to Brenton?

   After 4 days.

Look Back

7. When you set $y = y$ and plug your solution in, does your equation still hold true?

   Yes: $\frac{1}{4}(4) + 1$ = $\frac{1}{2}(4)$

   2 = 2

SECTION 8B Graphing Lines
SECTION B: Quiz for Lessons 5 Through 6

5 Direct Variation

1. The table shows how many miles Julia has traveled after riding so many hours on her bicycle. Make a graph of the data and tell whether the data sets have a direct variation.

   __yes__

Hours	Miles
0	0
1	9
2	18
3	27
4	36
5	45
6	54

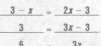

Find each equation of direct variation, given that y varies directly with x.

2. The variable y is 9 when x is 3.

   $y = 3x$

3. The variable y is 2 when x is 8.

   $y = \frac{1}{4}x$

4. The variable y is 4.5 when x is 4.5.

   $y = x$

5. The variable y is 5 when x is 0.5.

   $y = 10x$

6. The variable y is $\frac{7}{2}$ when x is $\frac{7}{2}$.

   $y = x$

7. The variable y is 2 when x is 6.

   $y = \frac{1}{3}x$

SECTION 8B Graphing Lines
SECTION B: Quiz for Lessons 5 Through 6, continued

6 Solving Systems of Linear Equations by Graphing

Solve each linear system by graphing. Check your answer.

8. $2x - y = 0$
   $x + y = 18$

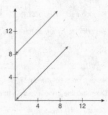

   point of intersection: __(6, 12)__

9. $x - y = 0$
   $y - x = 8$

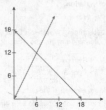

   point of intersection: __none__

10. The price of baseball tickets at Sunny Park and at Midnight Park has been increasing steadily since 2000. In 2000, Sunny Park was charging $3 less than the $6 they charged in '99. Sunny Park started charging $1 more each year after 2000. Midnight Park opened in 2000, and started tickets at $3. By 2006, Midnight Park was charging $9 per ticket. At what point were both parks selling baseball tickets for the same price?

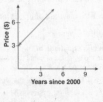

   They were both charging the same price all along.

   The equation of both lines is $y = x + 3$.

SECTION 8B Graphing Lines

SECTION B Enrichment: Solving Systems of Equations by Substitution

A system of linear equations can be written as a single equation in one variable and you can solve the system using substitution.

When the two equations are solved for y, you can set the expressions $(mx + b)$ equal to each other and solve for x.

When you know the value for x, you can solve for y.

Solve the linear system of $y = x + 10$ and $y = 5x - 10$.

$x + 10 = 5x - 10$	Set expressions equal to each other.
$10 = 4x - 10$	Subtract x from each side of the equation.
$20 = 4x$	Add 10 to each side of the equation.
$5 = x$	Divide each side by 4.

Substitute 5 for x in either of the original equations. $y = 5 + 10$.

The solution to the system is (5, 15).

You can check the solution by verifying that (6, 15) satisfies both of the original equations.

$y = x + 10$	$y = 5x - 10$
$15 = 5 + 10$	$15 = 5(50 - 10)$
$15 = 15$ ✓	$15 = 15$ ✓

Solve each system of linear equations using substitution.

1. $y = 2x - 1$ and $y = x - 8$

$(-7, -15)$

2. $y = 5x + 4$ and $y = -5x - 6$

$(-1, -1)$

3. $y = -x - 1$ and $y = -2x - 6$

$(-5, 4)$

4. $y = -4x + 2$ and $y = -2x$

$(-1, -2)$

Holt McDougal Mathematics

Holt McDougal Mathematics

LESSON 1 · Data, Prediction, and Linear Functions
Skills Intervention: Scatter Plots

A **scatter plot** shows a relationship between two sets of data. **Correlation** describes the relationship between the data sets. The **line of best fit** is a line that comes closest to the most points on the scatter plot.

Vocabulary
scatter plot
correlation
line of best fit

Describing Correlation from Scatter Plots
A teacher studying the effects of sleep on test scores gathered the data shown in the table. Use the data to make a scatter plot.

Label the x- and y-axes.

Determine and fill in the scale for each axis.

How many data points do you need to plot?
___14___

Plot the data from the table. For instance plot a point at (5, 69).

Hours Slept	Test Score	Hours Slept	Test Score
5	69	8.5	87
5	65	9	91
6	80	9	93
6.5	77	10	85
7	79	10.5	92
7	85	11	100
8	83	12	97

Test of Sleep

Does the data appear to have a positive, negative, or no correlation? __positive correlation__

How can you tell? __As the number of hours of sleep increases, the test scores increase.__

Using a Scatter Plot to Make Predictions
Make a scatter plot of the data and draw a line of best fit. Then use the data to predict how many boxes of cookies would be sold by someone who worked for 2 hours.

Boxes of Cookies Sold and Hours Spent Working						
Boxes of Cookies	46	50	60	50	73	75
Hours Spent Working	4	5	6	7	8	9

Draw a scatter plot.

Draw a line of best fit. It will have about as many points above the line as it does ___below___ the line.

According to the graph, someone who works 2 hours should sell about ___30___ boxes of cookies.

LESSON 2 · Data, Prediction, and Linear Functions
Skills Intervention: Linear Best Fit Models

Observe the Pattern
A study is conducted to measure the hours of sleep the night before an exam and the score of the exam.

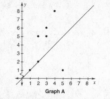

Answer these questions to describe the pattern.
Does the scatter plot appear to be linear or non-linear? __linear__

Does this mean that points appear to be on a line or not? __on a line__

Answer these questions to identify any clusters.
Is there a location where many points are grouped together? __yes__

If yes, at what locations? __when x = 8__

Answer these questions to identify any outliers.
Are there any points far away from other points? __yes__

Write a sentence that summarizes the pattern in the scatter plot. __The data appear to be linear with a cluster when x = 8 and there is an outlier when x = 7.__

Assessing the Line of Best Fit
Compare the scatter plots of data and the lines of best fit shown. Tell which model better fits the data. Explain your answer.

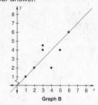

Graph A   Graph B

In Graph A, do the points follow the general direction of the line? __yes__
Are the points close to the line? __no__

In Graph B, do the points follow the general direction of the line? __yes__
Are the points close to the line? __yes__

On which graph are the most points closest to the line? __Graph B__

SECTION 9A · Data, Prediction, and Linear Functions
SECTION A: Quiz for Lessons 1 Through 2

1 Scatter Plots

1. Use the given data of class sizes to make a scatter plot.

Year	1999	2000	2001	2002	2003	2004	2005
Class size	235	264	216	385	372	361	406

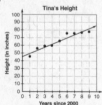
Class Size

2 Linear Best Fit Models
Find an equation for the line of best fit, and tell what the slope and y-intercept represent in terms of the data it models.

2.
Tina's Height

$y = 4x + 45$; the slope, 4, is the number of inches Tina grows each year. The y-intercept, 45 inches, is Tina's height in 2000.

3.
Population of a City
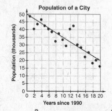

$y = -\frac{3}{2}x + 50$; the slope, $-\frac{3}{2}$, is the rate the population decrease each year, in thousands. The y-intercept, 50,000, is the population in 1990.

SECTION 9A · Data, Prediction, and Linear Functions
Section A Enrichment: Wingspan

A model plane contest had participants building their own planes in an attempt to travel the farthest distance. Different sized model airplanes were constructed to achieve the longest flight. The students made a table of their results.

Wingspan (in inches)	2	5	8	10	12	15	20
Flight distance (in feet)	10	16	20	24	30	36	44

1. Use the given data to make a scatter plot.

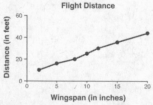
Flight Distance

Tell whether the data sets have a positive, negative, or no correlation. Explain.

2. the school year of the person launching the airplane and the flight distance

__no correlation; The grade of the person launching the plane has no affect on the distance it will travel.__

3. the weight of the landing gear attached to the plane and the distance flown

__negative correlation; The more weight the landing gear has, the shorter the flight will be.__

4. the tailwind speed and the distance traveled

__positive correlation; The greater the wind pushing the plane, the farther it will fly.__

5. Predict how far a model plan will fly if it has a 25-inch wingspan.

__about 55 feet__

Top Left Quadrant

Ready to Go On?

LESSON 3

Data, Prediction, and Linear Functions

Skills Intervention: Linear Functions

A **linear function** is the graph of a straight line. **Function notation** shows that the output of function f corresponds to input value x and is written $f(x)$.

Vocabulary
linear function
function notation

Identifying Linear Functions

Determine whether $f(x) = \frac{1}{2}x + 3$ is linear. If so, give the slope and y-intercept of the function's graph.

$f(x) = \frac{1}{2}x + 3$

Graph the function.

What is the y-intercept? __3__

What is the slope? $\frac{1}{2}$

What shape is the graph? __straight line__

The function __is__ linear.

Writing the Equation for a Linear Function

Write the rule for the linear function.

What is the general form of a linear function?
__$f(x) = mx + b$__

What is the y-intercept from the graph? $b =$ __2__

Substitute the value of b into the equation. $f(x) = mx +$ __2__

Use $(-2, 0)$, another point on the graph, and substitute the x- and y-values into the equation.

$f(x) = mx + 2$

$0 = m(-2) +$ __2__   Substitute $x =$ __-2__ and $y =$ __0__.

$0 = -2m +$ __2__   Multiply.

$\dfrac{-2}{} = -2m$ Isolate the variable.

$\dfrac{-2}{-2} = \dfrac{-2m}{-2}$ What do you divide both sides by?

$\underline{1} = m$ Solve for m.

Substitute the values for m and b into the function.

The rule is $f(x) = \underline{1}\,x + \underline{2}$.

113   Holt McDougal Mathematics

Top Right Quadrant

Ready to Go On?

LESSON 3

Data, Prediction, and Linear Functions

Problem Solving Intervention: Linear Functions

Sometimes you can use graphs to estimate and then use equations to find the exact solutions.

The graph shows a 13,000-gallon swimming pool being filled at the rate of 300 gal/hr. The pool is half full at 3:15 P.M. on May 21. There was already some water in the pool when the filling started at 10:00 P.M. on May 20. When will the pool be full?

Understand the Problem

1. How long did it take for the pool to be half full?

   $17\frac{1}{4}$ (or 17.25) hours

2. The point where the pool was half full is marked on the graph. Label the point with its coordinates.

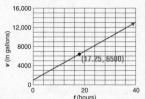

Make a Plan

3. If you knew the equation of the graph, how could you find when the pool will be full?

   Substitute 13,000 for v and solve for t.

Solve

4. Find m, the graph's slope.   300 gal/hr

5. Substitute to find b.

   $v = m\,\underline{t} + \underline{b}$

   $6500 = 300 \cdot \left(17\frac{1}{4}\right) + \underline{b}$

   $b = 1325$

6. Find t when $v = 13,000$. When will the pool be full?

   $v = 300t + 1325$, $13{,}000 = 300t + 1325$, $t = 38\frac{11}{12}$; at 12:55 P.M. on 5/22

Look Back

7. Why should it take more than $17\frac{1}{4}$ hours to fill the second half of the pool?

   Sample answer: There was water in the pool when the filling started.

114   Holt McDougal Mathematics

Bottom Left Quadrant

Ready to Go On?

LESSON 4

Data, Prediction, and Linear Functions

Skills Intervention: Comparing Multiple Representations

Comparing Slopes

Find and compare the slope for the linear functions g and h.

$g(x) = 3x - 4$

x	2	3	4	5
$h(x)$	7	5	3	1

Is $g(x)$ written in slope-intercept form? __yes__

What is the slope-intercept form? __$y = mx + b$__

What is the slope of $g(x)$? __3__

Use the slope formula to find the slope of $h(x)$.

What is the difference in y-coordinates? __2__

What is the difference in x-coordinates? __-1__

What is the slope of $h(x)$? __-2__

Which function has a greater slope? __g__

The slope of __g__ is greater than the slope of __h__.

Comparing Intercepts

Find and compare the y-intercepts for the linear functions p and q.

x	0	2	4	6
$p(x)$	3	5	7	9

$q(x) = \frac{3}{4}x + 2$

Does the table include a value for $p(x)$ when $x = 0$? __yes__

What is y-intercept of $p(x)$? __3__

Is $q(x)$ written in slope-intercept form? __yes__

What is the slope-intercept form? __$y = mx + b$__

What is the y-intercept of $q(x)$? __2__

Which function has a greater y-intercept? __p__

The y-intercept of __p__ is greater than the y-intercept of __q__.

115   Holt McDougal Mathematics

Bottom Right Quadrant

Ready to Go On?

SECTION 9B

Data, Prediction, and Linear Functions

SECTION B: Quiz for Lessons 3 Through 4

3 Linear Functions

Determine whether each function is linear.

1. $f(x) = \frac{4}{7}x - \frac{1}{7}$ __yes__   2. $f(x) = 1.85x + 9$ __yes__   3. $f(x) = 2x^4 + 1$ __no__

Write a rule for each function.

4.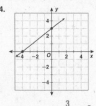

   $y = \frac{3}{4}x + 3$

5.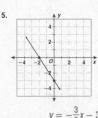

   $y = -\frac{3}{2}x - 3$

6. Angela has a base salary of $220 per week. She also earns a commission of $20 on every widget she sells. Find a rule for the linear function that describes Angela's weekly income if she sells x widgets. How much does Angela earn if she sells 8 widgets in one week?

   $f(x) = 20x + 220$; $380

4 Comparing Multiple Representations

Find and compare the slopes for the linear functions f and g.

7.

x	1	2	3	4
$f(x)$	0	-2	-4	-6

and
$g(x) = -\frac{1}{2}x + 3$

slope of f is -2; slope of g is $-\frac{1}{2}$; the slope of g is greater than the slope of f.

8.

x	$f(x)$
-2	-5
-1	-2
1	4
2	7

slope of f is 3; slope of g is 3; the slope of f and g are both 3.

116   Holt McDougal Mathematics

SECTION 9B Data, Prediction, and Linear Functions

Section B Enrichment: What You Are and What You Are Not

What are you about as a person? This activity will try to answer that question for you.

First, graph each of these four linear functions.

1. $f(x) = 2x + 4$

2. $f(x) = -\frac{1}{2}x + 4$

3. $f(x) = 2x - 6$

4. $f(x) = -\frac{1}{2}x - 1$

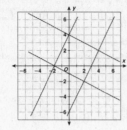

What figure is in the center? ___square___

This figure is telling you what you are not.

Now graph each of these five linear functions.

5. $f(x) = 3x + 3$

6. $f(x) = -3x + 3$

7. $f(x) = -\frac{2}{3}x - 1$

8. $f(x) = \frac{2}{3}x - 1$

9. $f(x) = 1$

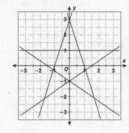

What figure is formed by the graphs you draw? ___star___

This figure is telling you what you are.